Tuscany...
NEXT LEFT

RANDALL STEVEN ALTIG

PAGE PUBLISHING, INC.
New York, NY

First originally published by Page Publishing, Inc. 2016

ISBN 978-1-68139-827-3 (pbk)
ISBN 978-1-68139-828-0 (digital)

Printed in the United States of America
Cover Design by Sharon Altig-Smith

CONTENTS

ACKNOWLEDGEMENTS

My Mom has been a constant support in my life and writing process, a proverbial sounding board, letting me know by her laughter that I was heading in the right direction with this story. During the process she would always say, "Call me tomorrow and read me more of what you have written, I can't wait to hear what happens next".

To my Father, thank you for giving me life and so much more.

My Friend, Dr. Charles Thompson…He has helped me to understand the meaning of turning left while teaching me how to hear, follow and feel the voice and language of my heart.

CAST OF CHARACTERS

(In alphabetical order after Randy)

Randy – this is his story

Alto – midget greeter in Capri

Anastasia – Samuele's sister in law

Andrea – front desk manager at the St. Regis, Rome

Angela – Peter's friend

Angelo – Stella's rescue dog

Antonio – raft guide to Capri

Batia – daughter of Morty and Chava

Chava – tourist in Capri, wife of Morty

Christiano – driver and guide

Claudio – Samuele's good friend

David – Randy's nephew

Giada– Samuele's mom

Jackie – Randy's friend

Julie – David's girlfriend

Kellie – Randy's niece

Manuel – shopkeeper in Florence

Marie – Mark's wife

Mark – Randy's brother

Max – Manuel's friend

Michael – Randy's friend

Morty – tourist in Capri, husband of Chava

Natasha – Randy's niece

Nicole – Jackie's niece

Noah – son of Chava and Morty

Peter – Randy's nephew

Ping Li – Jackie's friend and next-door neighbor

Ricardo – restaurant owner at the beach

Samuele –Mark's friend

Sandro – Samuele's brother

Sienna – Samuele's girlfriend

Sofia – Samuele's daughter

Stacy and George Vineland – auction bidders

Stefano – front desk manager, Buca di Bacco hotel

Stella – lives next door to the villa

Tina – Samuele's wife

Toby – Randy's soon to be nephew

Tom – Jackie's ex-husband

CHAPTER 1

The Call

Many Americans dream for the opportunity to take their trip of a lifetime, and most would say that trip would be to Italy, in the region of Tuscany, a magical place entwined by hillsides dressed in rolling vineyards, dotted with storybook family restaurants serving the best food and wine while offering bike rides through the country, art steeped in history in an area that defines a carefree notion that life can imitate art if you live it the right way. Ah, the romance of it all!

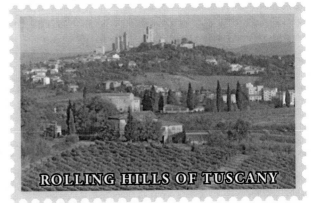

ROLLING HILLS OF TUSCANY

Now I have to admit that on some level I was beginning to get intoxicated with the idea. And how can you not when every cooking and travel show on television and most lifestyle magazines on the newsstands are devoting the majority of their programming and articles to the Italian way? It seems like they really know how to do it—food, fashion, cars, life. What do they know that I don't? Can I ever learn it in my fast-paced American life, or did I miss out because I never took Italian as a second language, never studied abroad, nor was I brought up as a Catholic.

I know, maybe I could start with Rosetta Stone in the privacy of my home, learn conversational wine terminology, and start wearing skinny Italian jeans just to heighten the effect of the social interaction at those casually coiffed dinner parties dotted with newly single women in plunging neck-lines with too much divorce money. You know the ones who never learned not to choke a wine glass and are still reeling from the setbacks they experienced from their unfaithful mul-timillionaire husbands. But then again maybe the wineglass is a metaphor for the ex-husbands, and now they're looking for their trip of a lifetime. I'll explain this all in more detail a little later, but for now we can just sum it up into two words: *poetic justice.*

Early one weekend morning when I was trying to sleep in, my phone rang. I listened to hear the faint delayed voice on the other end of the line, "Randy are you there?"

"Yes, who is this?"

"It's your brother. You're not going to believe it, I just came over to Italy for few days with a friend of mine who has been hounding me to make good on the promise that I would one day go to Italy with him. He wanted me to meet his family, see his family business, and last but not least, introduce me to a statue of himself in front of his high school."

"Who is it?" I asked.

"Oh you know Samuele who owns the Italian restaurant and gelateria in town, it's him."

"Really," I replied, "I had no idea he had a statue," as I thought to myself, but why wouldn't he?

"So," he went on to say, "since it was a quick trip, we left our wives at home and—are you ready for this? Their family has a four-hundred-year-old villa in Tuscany, and they possibly want to sell it, but first I need you to see it and see what can be done with it."

Knowing I was always good at taking the diamond in the rough, giving it the perfect cut and placing it in the best setting, so to speak, I said, "Great," without much thought. "I'd love to see it, let's do it!"

As I hung up the phone my mind began to run away from me with ideas of wonderment, possibilities, and excitement as to what a great adventure this could be. I was actually going to be in my own version of the movie *Under the Tuscan Sun*, and before I knew it I was off to Tuscany, Italy, with a suitcase in one hand and the sense of adventure in the other. Oh and did I mention I was also bringing additional supplies (clothing and such) for my brother Mark and sister-in-law Marie, whom we're meeting me there? They had already been at the villa for a few weeks getting a lay of the land, and during that time the temperature had gone from mild temperate mid-seventies to thick hot and humid mid-nineties.

Okay, so I have to quickly tell you about Samuele. He is a great guy, and he means really well. It's just that when he is around, there isn't a lot of room for anything else, sort of like a tight pair of pants on a Bee Gees brother. And rightfully so, I guess considering he did meet his blonde American expat wife, Tina, during the height of the disco era dancing the night away to the thumping beat of Donna Summer's *Last Dance* in a converted mid-eighteenth century building in downtown Florence, Italy. So at this point you may be thinking, "Okay, so what's the problem?" Well let me put it this way: The problem is that the 70s music has stopped, but he didn't and to this day neither he nor his clothes have relaxed. You'll understand the complete picture with him shortly.

Once the plane left the United States for Europe and I settled into my seat to embark on my adventure, I started to think I was never going to get there. I was squished between the window and an oversized—or should I say supersized—person who didn't realize we were not both sitting in the same seat. Her stomach was like a large squid engulfing our shared armrest as if it had just found another meal. I tried counting backwards, I tried listening to relaxing music on my iPhone, I even tried holding my breath and getting in touch with my chakras—anything to go to sleep and escape where I was. Unfortunately, when I was finally able to get myself into a quasi-state of relaxation and indulge in an extremely brief nap, I awakened to find the side of this person's leg and stomach squishing down on my arm, her head tilted, yes, in my direction with her mouth open, breathing on me last night's dinner, and by the smell of it I actually thought I had stepped in something.

That's it, I thought, this has to change, so ever so gently I tried to move her stomach and leg off of my numb arm without accidentally awaking her. But as my luck would have it, she woke up and looked at me with her one big eye and asked in a sort of nondescript voice, "Oh, do you need something?"

"Oh no," I said, "just adjusting my arm," as my mind was fighting with me to say, "Yes, I need you to move the ham hock and side of beef into your own seat!" Shortly thereafter she began to knit a scarf she explained she had to have finished before she got to Italy. I knew I was in for a long ride as she sat there clicking the knitting needles over and over and over. The sound of those needles constantly clicking was as bad as having water slowly dripped on your forehead; in fact, I think they even have a name for it: Chinese water torture.

I've always heard it's good to "embrace your fears," and if I was going to be sleeping next to, partially under, or with her again within the next few hours, I needed to at least introduce myself, know her name, and embrace the motto since at that very moment this person was my biggest fear. "I'm

Randy," I said, *and don't get excited I'm not what you may have heard the name means*, I thought.

"Oh, nice to meet you," she replied, "I'm Pat." Good thing I didn't guess her name 'cause I had her pegged for an androgynous Chris. Maybe it was because of the khaki pants, blue broadcloth button down, ninja haircut and pocket protector.

While the plane was making its approach onto the runway in Tuscany, I looked out at the hundreds of villas dotting the countryside wondering if it was one of those, and if so, which could it be. Then all of a sudden my thoughts were interrupted by the landing of the plane and bouncing of the wheels. Never did I realize the flight I was just on was nothing compared to the ride I was now getting ready to take!

Carousel number one was where we had all been instructed our luggage would be once we got inside the terminal. I found that sort of humorous considering there was only one carousel for luggage; maybe they were just confirming my luggage was going to show up. Sure enough after about fifteen minutes, here they came, all four suitcases. Once I had it all loaded on the cart with my two additional carry-on pieces, my cart looked like the Leaning Tower of Pisa, secure at the bottom and leaning very heavy on top. *Gently, walk very gently and slow*, I told myself as I was trying to navigate through all of the oblivious and jetlagged people. Then lo and behold, out of nowhere Pat showed up right in front of my cart and dropped her knitting. I couldn't stop in time. You guessed it; the scarf got caught in the wheel and brought it to an immediate halt toppling over the Leaning Tower of Pisa onto her. I felt bad, but at that very moment I knew she understood what it was like to have something on top of you that was heavy and not yours.

With everything carefully restacked on the cart, I proceeded to exit the "secure" area to be greeted by a heat wall of humidity once I walked out the doors. As I looked around trying to locate my brother and sister-in-law, all I could see were a sea of small cars waiting to be rented and an abundance of people coming and going speaking a language where using their hands seemed mandatory and over talking each other was a way of life.

Within minutes here came the navy blue metallic rented family Fiat, not much bigger than the luggage cart I was pushing. I could see Mark driving crazy and Marie laughing. I knew right away why she was laughing: Mark knows I get extremely car sick especially in small cars, and Marie knew exactly what was going through my mind: *How is this going to happen?* Six bags, three adults, one small Fiat, and a partridge in a...Almost sounds like lyrics to a Christmas song.

We actually did it, shoving everything into the car as tight as a can of Cento Italian sardines. Our faces were pushed up against the windows, air condition was on full blast, and music from Richard Smith's *Tangos* album serenaded us from my iPhone while we laughed through the winding streets of Tuscany on the way to the villa out in the countryside.

The scenery was breathtaking. Rolling hills, vineyards, poppy and sunflower fields among old stone and stucco homes washed in warm

POPPY FIELDS OF TUSCANY

colors of lemon yellows, earthy browns, papaya reds, and Tuscan tan all wearing top hats of red tile that defines the romantic vision of Tuscany.

"We're almost there," they told me after we had been in the car for what seemed to be forever. "Just up around the next bend in the road and then a left turn," Marie said. *Yeah, Tuscany, next left,* I thought with my face pressed up against the window. Then I saw what looked to be a very old rock wall almost like it belonged to some kind of medieval fortress, and that's where we took our last major turn. Actually a hard left turn right across from a small grayed-out wooden sign on the side of the road that read Chianti. Hmm, did that mean we were actually Chianti adjacent?

FORTRESS WALL

One more immediate left turn at the first corner next to the grocery store, sort of a grocery store. It's one of those upstairsdownstairs situations where the owners live upstairs and come downstairs to open the store when they want, otherwise you ring the bell at the door, and the lady comes down and opens it. She stocks basic provisions almost like an extremely rustic AM/PM, except she has the fresh artisan cheeses and meats you could only find in the U.S. at a specialty store. She seems like a nice lady, considering I can't understand anything she is saying. I let her count the money in my hand, and then she grabs it like an organ-grinder monkey. There is sort of an immediate authentic trust. It's all just part of the deal I guess.

"We're here," they said with excitement in unison! I couldn't believe it. The back of the villa is right across from the store, and as the big iron gates started to open, I was lost in what was ahead. A structure standing before us, painted pale yellow with unpatched spots of stucco peeling back, exposing bricks lost somewhere in time. We all hurriedly stumbled out of the car. My legs felt like limp pasta, only to be revived by briskly jumping up and down in the canopy of the humid Tuscan air. Oh what a long day this had been—yes, this was all in one day, at least for me, and I hadn't really slept in over twenty-two hours.

CHAPTER 2

Lay of the Land

Apparently *la familia* next door have been living there for quite some time; as the story goes they have been farming the vineyards and taking care of the land for over three hundred years. I couldn't' wait to see what they all looked like! The lady of the house, Stella, has a self- appointed job around the villa and makes it her business to take care of overseeing things on the grounds when no one is there. I was looking forward to meeting her. I knew she had to have some good stories, I mean in three hundred years, something extraordinary has had to have happened.

My wish granted, I didn't have to wait long at all. Stella's watchful eye had seen us drive in, and within minutes out she came in her three-quarter-length summer print smock wrapped with an apron and waving hello with her dish towel as if she was surrendering. I wanted to say, "It's okay, I'm your friend," but right then Marie in her magical way of communicating with foreigners without speaking the language, started telling her that I was a relative who had just arrived from the United States.

THE VILLA

Wait, we're the foreigners, I then thought. Marie's interpretive dance moves continued, coupled with overly exaggerated hand gestures, and before long Stella seemed to know exactly what Marie was saying, and everyone was laughing.

As we opened the large arched wooden doors into the villa, I could see right away the potential of what could be done; room by room my imagination started to awaken. The old wood ceiling beams, tile and stone floors, the stucco walls—all had a story to tell of a history and life waiting to be nurtured and given a chance to live up to its full potential. And I knew I was the one who would have to bring it to life.

I decided to take the last room on the right down the hall at the top of the stairs; it was not being hit by the direct sun, so I knew it would be somewhat cooler. The bed was typical Italian, I was told: flat, very flat, one sheet, one blanket, a perfectly positioned dip right in the middle, or better yet more like a gutter, and of course a flat pillow with absolutely no hope of puffing it up no matter how hard I beat it and shook it. I opened the large wood-shuttered windows to bring in the afternoon breeze and to get some air moving. After lying down on the bed to rest for just a few minutes, I heard Marie yell down the hall. "Don't lay down whatever you do, you'll fall asleep, and you want to stay awake as long as you can. Also Samuele's family is coming over shortly to go to dinner with us. They want to meet you, and it won't go late I promise".

Sleep deprivation doesn't ever go well for me, so I got up with assistance from the old iron headboard, went into the bathroom to brush my teeth and splash water on my face to wake up. To the right of the sink were the toilet and a bidet. The toilet didn't have a flusher on it, which you never notice until it's too late. Not knowing what to do after going to the bathroom standing there in front of the toilet, I reached over and pushed in one of two sliver knobs embedded in the tile wall. Before I even knew what happened water shot out of the bidet and soaked the whole front of me up past my neck. I started to gag. Marie heard me and came running to the door. "Are you okay?" she said. And right when I was trying to tell her what happened she said, "Don't use the bidet, it's broken."

Really, I thought, *I never did. I only pushed a button and now I'm dripping wet!* Needless to say, I was now awake and ready for the second act of the day; no need to splash cold water on my face anymore!

"The in-laws are here," Mark yelled from the kitchen (an inside joke my brother and I have).

Not ours, I thought, as Mark continued to say, "Randy, Marie, hurry come down." We got down the stairs and to the front door just in time as they started parading in. Samuele's brother Sandro was the first to come in with his wife/girlfriend, her name is Anastasia, and of course, right behind them was Samuele and his wife Tina. I say or call Anastasia the "wife/girlfriend" because I wasn't sure. They may have mentioned it, but there was so much going on with her I got distracted, and I didn't want to ask questions. I would have had too many to ask, like "Are those real?" or "Is that real? Can you breathe in that outfit?" If you know who Ms. Wiggins is from the Carol Burnett show, well Anastasia could be her Italian twin.

She kept pulling down the bottom of her leopard print mini skirt but it didn't make any difference; it didn't move. Her thin black sleeveless top fit her like a compression bandage strapped over two big water balloons, and the shoes, well let's just say they would definitely be a pole dancer's dream. They were tall with leopard print and an acrylic platform heel, but enough with the compliments. I'm sure she is probably a really nice person, just misunderstood, and I don't mean because I don't speak Italian.

Sandro doesn't pay much attention to her; she seems to be more of a hood ornament for him if you know what I mean. Tina, on the other hand, also seemed nice but somewhat anxious. She was tall with overly bleached, damaged and blow dried snow bunny blonde hair; I'm sure the carpet didn't match the drapes. She looked like she could have possibly been a model in her earlier days, but she definitely peaked about 25 years ago. You could tell she still knew how to work the makeup brush and had overly mastered the "smokey eye." Her outfit was one of those "oh I just threw it together" sexy casual looks, but I could also tell she put a lot of thought into it because from any angle I could see she was only a glass of wine and a snap or button away from an intentional wardrobe malfunction. Whoops!

Next in the parade of relatives was Samuele's mother, Giada. I'm sure you would agree that most women you see carry a purse; his mom carries an aluminum pan of food. I didn't realize before we left for dinner we were having appetizers she had prepared. Now, she doesn't even ask you if you want any; she just dishes it up and hands it to you and yells, "Mangia!" I figured out that means *eat!*

So that's what I did, but I could hardly chew it. The more I chewed it, the more I thought I was going to throw up in my mouth thinking whatever this is, it's not going down. I asked Marie what it was. She said she thought it was eggplant parmigiana. Then I asked her if Giada owned an orthotics factory, and she started to laugh. Knowing I was going to choke if I didn't get something to drink, I told her it wasn't funny and to please get me some water fast.

Right then as I'm starting to perspire with this hard piece of eggplant stuck between the roof of my mouth and my throat, Giada turned around, looked at me, and in Italian said, "Ah, you want more," and she dropped another petrified eggplant pinwheel on my plate. All I can say is, thank God for big paper napkins.

Last but not least was Samuele's best friend Claudio. He walked in a few minutes later. He's a middle-aged typical Italian macho guy. Well, at least he thinks, but actually he is more cheesy suave if anything, and I'd say heavier on the cheese than on the suave. He is a big smoker but never alone; he always makes sure there is a glass of wine in the other hand as a companion while he walks around like a dog in heat. He is the single guy at the party whose story always ends the same: she got away. And I say good for her.

As we all got into our national cars of Italy, miniature Fiats, la familia passive-aggressively hurried to find a seat as if the music was getting ready to stop in a game of musical chairs. Luckily I had the keys to one of the cars, so I knew I would have a seat for sure. I purposefully lagged a little behind everyone so I could watch Anastasia navigate the gravel driveway in those acrylic stripper heels while trying to get her extra-long legs into the munchkin car. I was envisioning one of those Hanes commercials from the 1970s where the super model's limo is at the red carpet. Someone opens the door while a set of beautiful long legs in a pair of high-fashion pumps unfold from the back seat followed by the most stunning girl you have ever seen, you know the type; but in this case it wasn't a super model, and it wasn't a limo. It was a gnome mobile, and I didn't know how those legs were going to either fold up or out of that car, but she handled it like a seasoned pro. She got into the backseat, flipped one leg up on the center console while bending the other up under her chin.

My sister once had a Nurse Julia Barbie doll that could also do that after I accidentally broke her leg out of the socket when I looked up her dress to investigate. I was nine. But that's another story. Anyway, off we went in single file out the villa's gates, driving down the serpentine country road to an exceedingly charming stucco restaurant sitting in the middle of a pasture. *Oh this is going to be good*, I thought. I wasn't only thinking about the food but about Anastasia wobbling through the pasture in those heels.

While pulling off the main road over a few grassy bumps onto a gravel driveway, I could see the full restaurant come into view. Off the back of the building was a large open air porch with white gauze floor-to-ceiling drapery panels gently blowing in the evening breeze. As we approached the entrance you could see lit candles everywhere casting shadows of dancing shapes onto the color-washed stucco walls. Fire flies were waking up to entertain us with an evening serenade of light in the fields off the veranda. All of this was setting the stage for my first night in Tuscany, and a magical one at that.

"Baaabe, come here," Samuele said to the waitress in a tone that had probably worked in his favor thirty years ago in a disco, but he was definitely pushing it now. And if it wasn't for him ordering the most expensive wine on the menu, I am sure our evening meal would have been a disaster because you could just tell the server was not going to have any of that macho Italian talk toward her at any table she was attending. As she poured the wine, I was notified by my brother that I really needed to have a glass. I don't drink alcohol very often, and when I do it generally ends up being only a few sips. So it was a big decision to have a glass because I knew if I had a glass and didn't like it, the wine bottle wouldn't be the only thing with a label at the table; I would be given one too. Sure enough just at that point when the wine touches your mouth and you instantly know, I knew I couldn't drink it.

I quietly told Marie she could have my wine if she wanted while Mark in his best broadcasting voice said from the other end of the table, "What's wrong, Randy, don't you like it?"

"No, not really," I said.

"Oh, don't worry, you'll like it soon, you just have an immature palette." That was a new one. I had never heard that before. I wanted to ask him, "Oh, is that why you don't like lima beans?"

As the wine poured freely like water from a fountain, everyone seemed to lose track of space and time, except of course for me. See what is good to understand before you go to Italy is that dinner in Tuscany starts at about 8 p.m. and isn't over until at least 10 or 11 p.m., and I honestly don't know how they do it. Heavy meals of pasta, beef, chicken, rabbit, pheasant and other choice meats that skew from my American white Anglo Saxon upbringing, along with cheeses, olives, salads, bread, and wine, wine, and more wine. Did I say wine? Followed by dessert and, of course, coffee, espressos to be precise—espressos at 10 p.m., really? Yes, to relax you and help you to sleep, and guess what, it works. I don't know why, but it does, and by that time it didn't matter anyway. I was so over the whole notion of looking sexy at dinner in Italy, I was exhausted. All I wanted to do was to go back and get into bed. Even that flat Italian bed in my room seemed to become luxurious in my mind. You know they say that feeling sexy isn't all in how you look but how you feel. Well thank goodness I was traveling and sleeping alone because by this time I felt full on so many levels.

Waking up on my first day in Tuscany, I was greeted by the wonderful aroma of fresh bread. The grocer behind the villa also has wood-burning bread ovens where they cook fresh bread daily for the people in the village. My bedroom is positioned just perfectly so that the early morning breeze carries the fresh baked essence right through the shuttered windows every morning. Now that's my idea of the perfect alarm clock.

With such a dramatic time shift going to Italy, it is strange how you can somehow wake up the next morning feeling rested. Maybe it was because my reality was laced with so much excitement about what was going to unfold during my first full day in Tuscany. As I jumped out of bed I couldn't wait to take a shower and get ready. My options were to choose either the shower downstairs that was all part of a tub with a half-glass door system that folds open, making you feel like you're stepping into a pantry replete with a slow drain. Or I could also choose the one down the hall from my room that sort of looked like an oversized YMCA tiled stall with a nozzle that was positioned so the whole bathroom floor would flood when in use. And then of course there was the one in the master bedroom, which in my opinion should always be the nicest, most luxurious one in the house. Well this one looked like a hybrid of a TSA security scanner and the oxygen chamber that Michael Jackson slept in. It must be from all of my time spent traveling, but I had a feeling if I got in that plastic shower capsule I would feel obligated to throw my arms up in the air and wait for someone to tell me to go ahead and step out, the scan was completed. Apparently that was a standard sort of prefab shower system they use in Italy when they put in new showers. *What about Italian tile*, I thought, *aren't they supposed to be known for that?* It was all too much to think about right then, so I chose the YMCA tiled stall and used lots and lots of towels.

Once I finished showering and mopping up the floor with all the towels, I got dressed and went downstairs to put all of the wet towels in the washing machine. Of course the washer and dryer were from Germany with all the directions in German. So I called for Marie to help me figure it all out. She doesn't speak or read German either, but remember she does have a special ability with foreign language that I don't seem to have. She has also raised four children, so she knows her way around a washer and dryer pretty well. We finally got it going after a few trial and errors and were then free to go have breakfast.

When I walked into the kitchen, to my surprise, my brother had already been next door to buy the fresh morning bread, orange Tuscan melon, fresh prosciutto, eggs, and coffee. It couldn't have been a more perfect breakfast, especially the melon slices wrapped with fresh prosciutto. I felt like I was actually living in a real life movie, except it was our own with no cameras.

The buzzer went off to let us know the laundry had finished washing, and it was now ready to go into the dryer. Who would know that doing the laundry would be such an event? I took the towels out of the washer and put them in the dryer, turned the dial to the full drying time, and pushed the button to start, but nothing happened. I tried it again, nothing happened. *Great*, I thought, *it's broken. How am I going to dry heavy wet towels?* I called Marie again to come help figure it out, and she came in and tried the settings routine again, but nothing happened. As we were standing there looking at the dryer as if it was going to talk to us, Marie saw a handle at the bottom of the dryer. She pulled on it, and out came a plastic water tank reservoir that looked like it should be on a Jurassic Super Soaker water gun. It was full of water, we finally figured out that the dryer doesn't evaporate the water into hot air or steam and exhaust it to the outside like in America. What it does is pull the water from the clothes and condenses it into the tank. When the tank is full of water, the dryer doesn't work until you empty the tank. *Of course*, I thought, *we should have known*, but little did I know that this was only the beginning to understanding more than a new language. It was going to be an adventure in understanding a new way of thinking.

I spent the rest of the morning going room by room in the villa, sketching out elevations of walls, windows, doors, and doorways while at the same time taking pictures of each room and its special features so that when I got back home I could make sure I was able to design each space accurately and efficiently without solely relying on what I had committed to memory. What I realized though when I returned home to the United States was I had forgotten to put measurements to each space, which I know ended up causing me premature hair loss and what my dentist called nighttime grinding. How could I have forgotten to do the most basic element of the design process? All I could think of was to blame it on the tiramisu I had eaten the night before.

We spent the next few days doing some sightseeing and getting a general overall feel for the quaint town, its people, the shops, and the daily activities that drive this beautiful northern Italian culture. The city center of Florence is quite breathtaking, especially when you look upon it from one of the designated hillside vantage points. The architecture and design of the city is built on a foundation of art. It's every-where you look—it's in everything they do, in the way they dress, and in the food they eat. I was quickly beginning to understand that for what I thought was intentional was sim-ply the way in which this culture thinks and does, it is all just a way of life—simple form over complex function.

CHAPTER 3

A Day at the Beach and More

F our of my nieces and nephews (Mark and Marie's kids) and a few others were flying into Florence from the U.S. in the next few hours. We were going to go pick them up, which meant we also needed to rent one more Fiat at the airport to fit everyone, then off to dinner and home. All of us decided to call it an early night since we had all voted to take a family adventure to the beach the next day. We weren't sure what beach we were going to, but we didn't need to worry about that because Samuele had previously called during dinner to find out what we were all doing tomorrow. Mark told him we were all going to the beach. He said, "Great, don't worry about a thing, I will call my friend who owns a restaurant down on the beach who will set us up, chairs, food, everything. Tina and I will see you in the morning." Wow, we all thought this should be fun even if our plans were derailed from having a "family" day at the beach.

The next morning we all awoke to the smell of fresh bread and coffee, had breakfast and pulled all of our bathing suites, towels, and a change of clothes together. We were not really sure what the day had in store, so we needed to be prepared for, well anything and everything. This was going to be a real adventure. We all got situated who was going to be in each car and identified who could read a map in motion without getting sick. The list started to narrow as to who would sit in the front passenger seat. Of course my car was the coolest, just because it was.

My nephew David with the longest legs sat in the front seat. He is about 6'4", but because he is thin he even looks taller. He needed to be able to stretch his legs and he could read the map in motion without getting sick so it worked out perfect for everyone. His girlfriend Julie was in the backseat, in the middle with beach bags on one side of her and my niece Kellie, who is a real supermodel in the making, on the other side. Julie was a very nice and cute girl, unassuming and ready to have a good time. She had a little bit of a lazy eye, but no one talked about it. I just have to say I thought it was kind of a strange phenomenon because it seemed to come and go, sort of a "now you see it now you don't" deal, kind of like what I thought her relationship with David would end up to be—short-lived, which thank goodness it was.

David was set up with a map, his cell phone, and a walkie-talkie programmed to talk to the walkie-talkie Mark and Marie had in their car. That way we could communicate for free with each other, otherwise the cell phone charges would have cost us more than a *Bruce Transgender* sex change, I mean you know, just guessing. Mark and Marie had my niece Natasha and her soon-to-be-husband, Toby, in their car along with my other nephew Peter, who is about 6'3", who again looks taller than he is. We tested the walkie-talkies, communication was set to go and so off we went.

I followed Mark and Marie because they had direct communication with Samuele, and since he was meeting us at the beach they would get up to date directions from him as needed.

Once we got off the country roads and onto the freeway, everything seemed to be going along great. I was able to keep up with Mark's last-minute-decision driving habits, David was communicating with his mom on the walkie–talkies, and Julie and Kellie were in charge of the music, and in charge they were. They kept the tunes pumping while rocking the car to the beat with their sit-down dancing moves in the back seat. There was only one small issue, but I didn't want to say anything. While Julie was in the back busting a move to the song "Mercy" by Duffy, her head would bob and weave in my rearview mirror. It wouldn't have been much of a problem, except she had a bright yellow headband on with a gigantic yellow-and-orange polyester gerbera daisy glued to it, and that thing kept getting in my way every time I had to change lanes. All I wanted was a little "Mercy" and have her sit still. I was also really wishing Mark would just pick a lane and stay in it, which would have made things so much easier. And then my second wish on the trip came true, but almost to our own demise. Mark picked the far left lane, where he finally stayed, and was keeping up with traffic, driving between 80 and 100 miles per hour, which meant I had to do the same. I didn't feel safe driving that fast and so close, so I backed off about three car lengths and told David to radio to Mark's car and tell them to slow down. Right at the moment a car came out of nowhere going faster than us driving right up behind me. I knew he was there, but the yellow daisy kept him out of the rear view mirror, and when I looked in the side mirror to see where he was, he was gone. I thought he can't be that close that I can't see him, can he? Before I knew it he was on the right side of my car passing me. I slowed as he passed and squeezed in between our car and Mark's car. I guess Mark still thought it was me behind him, so he didn't pay much attention to the fact that this guy wanted him to move over, which is what we later found out you are supposed to do. In fact you're not supposed to even be driving in the left lane—it is a passing lane.

Not knowing, Mark stayed put. The guy got so mad that he swerved back into the right lane then drove up alongside of Mark and Marie's car and started side ramming their car. I couldn't believe what I was seeing. It all happened so fast, their hub cap flew off and started spinning and rolling backward toward us. Of course we all ducked as it flew over our car, like ducking was going to make a difference. David was trying to explain on the walkie-talkie to his parents what was going on, but they wouldn't listen. They kept yelling at us, "You idiots, what are you doing? Why are you ramming our car?" Finally they realized what was going on, that it wasn't us. Mark got out of the lane and pulled over. I also pulled over, and so did car number three.

I think the man in car number three thought I was going to be his ally, but to his surprise, when he jumped out of his car and ran up to our cars, my soon-to-be-nephew Toby jumped out of the car with his big lens camera and started taking pictures, a great paparazzi intimidation move on his part. The man was so mad he started screaming at Toby in Italian. Now this guy was about 5'3" with four-inch plat-forms, a fake black sparsely woven comb over, and a mus-cle shirt. I guess he thought he was intimidating in his bad Italian club wear, gold chains and saggy muscles.

Then all of a sudden there was a major game changer. David and Peter got out of the cars. Before we knew it, the big mouth Italian frog started running away like a scared Rocky Balboa mini me in platform heels. He jumped back in his car and sped off out of sight. It was all so quick we were all left standing there on the side of the road laughing in shock.

We then got back in our cars and continued on to the beach. What a great little side show that was for the day, but oh, there were so many more to come.

Within minutes Kellie and Julie had the music thumping again as we enjoyed the beautiful scenery along the Mediterranean coastline. "We're only about 30 minutes away, everybody. Samuele and Tina have beach chairs ready and snacks waiting," Marie said over the walkie-talkie. We all started to get hungry as we imagined a wonderful lunch at a beautiful beach on the Italian Riviera. Fresh frutti di mare, cioppino, creamy pesto shrimp pasta—all these flashes of food were running through my mind.

We had arrived. The beach was lined with shops and restaurants that were contemporary but housed in structures that looked like buildings from a 1940's movie. And the way it works is that the restaurants own and maintain the beach, beach chairs, umbrellas, and restroom/changing rooms in front of their establishments. It's all sort of a small beach club concept; everything is right there for you to have a wonderful day at the beach. As we started walking toward the beach like a single file line of hoarders with all our beach bags, gear, and games, Samuele called to say he was on his way to meet us out front. Sure enough here he came, all tan in his electric blue Speedo extremely happy and proud. It was hard for me to look actually because it was all so tight. It definitely gave a new definition to beach balls, and for the first time on the trip I was really happy about being able to look at the yellow daisy.

The beach club we were at was architecturally retro 1930.

BEACHES OF TUSCANY

Stucco with curved lines, painted dove white with azure blue accents. The owner, Ricardo, had installed a wood boardwalk all the way to the beach that divided the beach chairs into two sections all staged to take full advantage of the sun. Each set of chairs came with its own bright orange umbrella and a table for placing your drinks and snacks on for an easy carefree day at the beach. Once we got all situated, the first thing I wanted to do was head to the water, the Mediterranean. I knew I was only minutes away from seeing the people of the Riviera, perfect and sexy bodies bronzed like dark car-amelized sugar. I couldn't wait to check out the scene; it was going to be a true Bain De Soleil moment. I mean the Mediterranean is the playground for the rich and famous, and home to so many of those romantic movie backdrops I had fantasized being part of at some point in my life. Visions of Bridget Bardot or Sophia Lauren running toward me in slow motion was the scene I was looking for, but the more I looked, the more I realized I was going to be looking for a long time. Big, large, and fat purple jelly fish were what I saw everywhere on the beach, making it like a unique game of hopscotch just to try and walk on the beach let alone run. I then realized my fantasy of a beautiful woman running toward me in slow motion was not going to happen. First of all there was nowhere to run, and second of all most of the women had hair under their arms and several with it even on their legs, a real buzzkill for me. Then I thought maybe I should just go back to our beach chairs where I can relax and pretend in my mind for what I had hoped for, but what was I actually thinking anyway? This fantasy only happens in the movies!

As I lay on the beach lounger in the sun listening to the gentle surf, warming my body into a deep state of sleep, I was awoken by the fragrance of herbs, bread, garlic, and meat all cooking in Ricardo's beach restaurant. I couldn't lie there long before I started becoming bilingual. My stomach was talking to me in both English and Italian. I was ready to eat.

Ricardo and his wife were all too excited about the meal they were preparing for us, and so was I. While sitting around the tables they started bringing out the food; pastas, antipasti, red sauces, cream sauces, vegetables, bread, all served family style except of course for the fish. They had prepared a fish for each one of us. I'm not sure what kind it was, but it was definitely from the ocean and it fit perfectly on each plate. The only problem with the fish was that it was looking at me. I have a very hard time eating food that looks at me while I'm eating it. It's enough that it was killed, but then it lies there and looks at me as if saying, "Really, now you're going to eat me?"

I don't know, maybe it's just me, but I can't have a relationship with my food. It just sort of has to be there, nicely presented, and not provoking too much thought from me about the backstory. I made up the excuse that I was just eating pasta and sauces while I was in Italy, and that I hoped they didn't mind if I didn't have the fish today. I then took the plated fish and faced it toward Samuele so it could stare him down. I was sure someone else in the group would want more fish as it lay there shimmering in the sun like a wide eyed over botoxed celebrity soaking up the spotlight in a tattered lame gown.

I have now come to realize that people love to drink wine with exotic and off-the-grid food. I finally broke the code and now know why they do it; they have to kill the taste and the thought. Think about it: they take a bite, they drink, they take a bite, they drink, they take a bite—you get the idea. So really, what they are doing is killing the taste of the food until they are buzzed enough to not even realize what they are eating, how it tastes, where it came from, or if it's looking at them. This all saves the embarrassment for the people who claim to enjoy the "finer things in life" from spitting out their food. And ever notice with a lot of those people, their head goes back when they take the drink? We'll that's because it makes the food go back and down much faster, never really having to let the food sit on their palate. And then they wait. They will tell you the waiting between bites is to savor the experience. No, I don't think so. They are actually psyching themselves up to do it all over again. If the "exotic" food and preparations were that wonderful, people would pair them with basic water to savor the experience and the taste. But I don't want to call anyone out for trying to fit into the lifestyle of embracing cultural experiences and acting well heeled. Sweet breads, rocky mountain oysters, foie gras, anyone?

As we all were packing up to return to the villa, someone brought up the fact that the storied town of Pisa was on our return route. Since I had only really ever seen it on refrigerator magnets, calendars and travel magazines, I thought it would be a good idea to stop off, be touristy, and possibly pick up a small coffee table figurine. Everyone agreed to go, so off we went. Once we arrived and found parking, we had to navigate through small streets and vendors to find the park setting where the actual Leaning Tower is located. It's a pretty cool sight if you have never seen it. Like seeing your favorite movie star in person, first you stare as you sort of zone out and think, *I can't believe this is actually in front of me.* Then you come to and stare some more until you realize what you're doing and have to tell yourself it's time to move on. Some people have to touch it, others line up for their preset ticketed entry time to walk up the tower. Others opt to just take pictures, usually the optical illusion kind where you act as if you're pushing the tower back or you're leaning against it. It's all interesting and mindless, making for a fun way to wrap up a day at the beach.

While we were walking back to the car I stopped with my niece Natasha at a small table set up with leaning tower tchotchkes. As I was looking over the merchandise trying to make a quick buying decision, I heard a loud ruckus happening. We turned around and saw people quickly packing up their wares and taking off down the street, others just walking away from their stuff. I knew something was up and it wasn't good. Luckily we decided to leave and not buy anything because we found out the police were there arresting people for selling illegally, and we would have been caught in the middle of the leaning tower sting. Needless to say my memories were going to have to be the ones I had placed in my mind and not on my coffee table.

I had three days before flying back home to the U.S., so I really just wanted to relax, take in the scenery around the villa, and make sure that I left with a real sense of the surroundings since that is always an important element when designing a space, but another plan would start to unfold the next morning.

When we all awoke the next morning we could tell it was going to be a difficult hot day. The sky was clear, and there was a hazy stillness in the air that always signals a day where you want to be by water. We didn't want to stay inside all day, so we decided to drive into Florence, do some last-minute late-morning shopping, have some pizza for lunch, and then go to the Piscina, the public pool. I know, just the word itself conjures up visions of something we don't' even want to think about associated with a pool, but it was so hot we took our chances. Never something I would do alone, or even with another person, this had to be a group experience. We packed our swimsuits and towels, and off we went.

It was a perfect morning so far with a light warm breeze as we walked around town and shopped. One of us in the group sounded off the hunger alarm talking about pizza; we then realized it was time to eat, so we found a pizzeria and bought several large pizzas for lunch. We sat outside the pizzeria in a courtyard at one of their metal tables that were set in a circle around their *peeing boy fountain* and ate, talked, and laughed. I never understand those fountains; I mean, who is ever excited about seeing something pee when you're trying to eat or any time for that matter? But then again I guess the fountain was an example of good fortune considering his nose was gone but his penis was still intact and functioning even if being helped by an electric pump. Once we were done we were all ready to go swimming, or so I thought. I wasn't sure I really felt like it since I had just devoured so much cheese and pepperoni pizza I was afraid it would be a struggle just to stay afloat, but I didn't want to ruin the plan, so I said nothing. I just thought to myself, *this too shall pass, and hopefully not while I'm in the pool.*

We took out and unfolded the oversized family map to find the quickest route to the Piscina. Standing on the corner in a circle looking like we were about ready to break into a campfire song, we had found it. We got lucky and saw we were only four blocks away. Of course the group dwindled once reality of going to a Piscina actually hit, but I pushed on toward the adventure, as did my nephew Peter, my two nieces, and Marie. We left the others to do what they wanted in town, and off we went. Once we arrived you could see four large swimming pools in different shapes, several water features, and of course a lot of people. We proceeded to walk into the entrance and waited in line to pay. One by one we went through the turnstile; we made our plan where to meet once we were changed and then followed the signs: boy's dressing rooms to the right, and girls to the left.

The men's locker room was wide open with large lockers above the white painted cement floor. Once you leave the locker area the cement floor was painted light blue and shaped like a trough filled about three inches high with water that you had to walk through as you followed wall signs with the word Piscina written in dark blue above a red arrow, it was all starting to get complicated. Peter and I put on our swim trunks, and proceeded to walk in the water through what felt like a *human habitrail* winding our way around trying to find how to get out to the pool.

As we got to the exit, an attendant was standing there. He looked at us, shook his finger and said, "Oh no, no, no!"

Peter and I both said, "What?"

He looked at our swim trunks, pointed, and said again, "No, no, no."

We asked him what he meant by "no, no, no," what was wrong? He said we could not wear swim trunks in the pool; we had to wear "Speedo." My stomach immediately cramped.

It might have been the greasy pepperoni pizza I had for lunch, but I also knew we didn't have "Speedo", and why would we? I have never worn one. I had a quick flash of Samuele at the beach and froze thinking, *what are we going to do?*

Peter got so mad at the attendant he said, "No way, forget it!" He was going to get dressed, leave, and go find the others in town. I, on the other hand, figured this was a rite of passage for me, and no better place to do it than right there in a foreign country. As they say, when in Rome...

So Peter left, and I told the attendant I didn't have one. He said, "Follow me," so I did. I followed him back out to the front by the pay window and through the turnstile. By this time there was a huge line to get in. He pointed to a vending machine about six feet tall by three feet wide full of little clear plastic boxes. Each box had a Speedo rolled up in it. As I found myself standing there alone knowing the girls had to be worried and waiting, it made it even more difficult to figure out the instructions, so I had to resort to trying my luck. Next to each large round black selection button was a picture of a guy, torso to knees wearing a Speedo. Each picture was a different style Speedo: some high cut, some medium, and some low, but it wasn't just that simple. You then had to try and figure out the size of your, well let me just call it "your situation," and which style would fit best. There was the Hacky Sack–looking pouch, the avocado-size pouch, one that looked like a banana hammock and there was even one with a pad in it for the "less fortunate."

This was all taking way too long, and my breathing started to get short and shallow. I knew everyone in line had to be looking and laughing, and to make matters worse, once I figured out which one would probably be best for me, I put my paper euro into the feeder, and it spit it back out. *You have got to be kidding!* I thought, so I rubbed it back and forth over my knee, got it nice and smooth, and reinserted it, only for the machine to spit it back out again.

You all know the noise; it's the international vending machine noise that the feeder doesn't want to work. The air was now getting really hot. I was so embarrassed and nervous I started to sweat. I tried it one more time, third time is definitely a charm, and it took it! *Ker plunk*, I heard the plastic box hit the tray. I grabbed it and briskly walked past the turnstile and "Do Not Run" signs back into the men's room to change.

As I was standing in the changing room, clothes off, stomach full of pizza with Speedo in hand, not at all looking like the statue of David, I instantly realized there was no tag in this so-called swimming garment that could double as an oven mitt. I honestly didn't know the front from the back. I knew I had picked the safest design, but really, no tag? The front and the back looked almost exactly the same; I knew only one thing for sure, I had a fifty-fifty chance of getting it right. So on it went, one leg, two legs, snap it's on. Hurriedly I rushed passed the attendant, he smiled a sort of odd smile and within seconds of finding myself standing in a sea of people all in navy or black bathing suits, I realized something was wrong and why I got the odd smile from the attendant.

My Speedo felt like a tee shirt put on the wrong way. Not quite right but not enough to immediately notice. I looked down, and saw the front of me looking like a smashed fedora hat. I could only imagine what was going on in the back. *This isn't happening*, I thought, *I'm in you know where!* I ran back into the men's room and spun it around. Little did I know that Marie and my two nieces saw the whole thing and could hardly contain themselves as they were hiding in the pool ducking beneath the edge laughing to tears. The decision had to be made right then and there: we would also be building a pool at the villa.

Once we finished our Piscina adventure, arrived back at the villa, and everything was unpacked, we all went into the living room and sat around talking about our day. Sometimes during those conversations at the end of a tiring day, topics come up, and decisions are made that probably shouldn't be happening. The conversation started to turn toward my hair. No one could believe how curly and wavy my hair had become. Granted, I did have the ultimate all-day pool hair, which is only rivaled by all-day beach hair. But add that with humidity, and it's a recipe for...du-dun-du-dun-da! Big hair! It fit in with the whole carefree Italian lifestyle look, but it was getting a little long. I then made the mistake of saying I should probably get my hair trimmed before I went home. Also I was secretly thinking it would be sort of exotic to have a European haircut because longer hair is the style, and I was sure by having it done in Italy I could get the cut I had always wanted but for some reason could never achieve with any stylist back in the States.

Marie remembered that Anastasia was supposed to be one of the top hairdressers in town. Of course she is, I thought. Marie also said Anastasia would probably love to do a sexy euro cut on my hair for me. So Marie called her and set it up for the next day.

Anastasia showed up as scheduled, had me sit at the kitchen table. She wet my hair and pulled out her scissors. I explained what I wanted, and she seemed to understand as she patted me on the shoulder and said in broken English, "No worries." That should have been my first worry. The second worry should had been when her breasts kept hitting me in the back of the head, and third when she didn't give me a mirror. What I can tell you is this. Anastasia who thinks she is a magician with her scissors can only make one thing disappear—your hair!

Just picture Little Cesar, and you know the rest of the story. My baseball hat became my best friend for the next two days until I got home and could have someone fix my "summer euro cut." What I learned from that experience were three things: Never under estimate the power of a mirror during a haircut. Second just because someone has an accent, it doesn't mean they know what they're doing. And third, exotic is a figment of our imaginations created by our desires for something different, because that's exactly what you will end up with.

CHAPTER 4

We've Only Just Begun

After I arrived home and was able to get through the reverse commute jet lag coming back to the United States from Europe, which generally takes one week for recovery, I was ready to start organizing the task at hand of interior designing the villa. The one caveat I had been informed about that I would have to remember was that villas are in Italy, chateau's are in France, and a villa is one step up from a house.

As I mentioned earlier, I didn't realize until I returned home that I had forgotten to put the measurements to each room on my villa drawings. The specific measurements were the elevations of windows, positions of doorways on walls, and closet dimensions. And because of my distracted oversight, it would mean I would have to call Arnoldo, the architect in Italy, and get the plans for the villa which I was hoping would have the information I needed.

The time zone in Florence during that time of year was eight hours ahead of me from my home on the West Coast in the U.S. So that would mean I would have to call him either before 5 a.m. or between 8:00 and 8:30 a.m. Pacific time so I could reach him before or after *riposo*. Riposo is the cultural excuse to stop working and take a midday nap. Now that's something I could usually go for, but in this case it wasn't. I chose to take my chances and take the later time window in hopes I could stay on my sleep schedule and still reach him. I was lucky, it worked and I was able to get ahold of him! Once I explained to Arnoldo what I needed and was sure he understood, we agreed he would e-mail all of the necessary information over to me the next day. Sure enough he did; the only problem was he sent it all to me in metric. So now I had to go through conversion, and I don't mean with my religious beliefs. I had to convert each dimension from metric to English, and once I was finished I can say, both conversions definitely require hope and prayer—a lot of it.

Now I have written articles on interior design and architecture for many years. I have even been published in newspapers and magazines, even designed some very imaginative homes on every scale from apartments to multimillion-dollar dream homes, but I have never revived a four-hundred-year-old villa, and from so far away. But I was up for the task, and I knew this opportunity would go down in history, as if a four-hundred-year-old history wasn't enough.

Once I got all of the plans converted and redrawn, the next job would be to space plan. This is where you apply the layout of the furniture within the blue print drawings. What goes where, what goes next to what, making the flow of the intention work at its optimum. Then I set out to get as much assistance as I could from the "experts" at the design centers to make my job easier. I needed to see fabrics, lighting, rugs, and more. Whatever was available for this specific project, I wanted to see and source from the best places I could. Everything has to be thought out, from salt and pepper shakers to mattress sets. You quickly realize with so many details that organization becomes one of your most prized everyday companions. In addition, I didn't have a lot of time to get this done because I had shipping container deadlines to Italy that needed to be met.

In the first design center I went to, a lady walked up to me a few minutes after her perfume showed up. She wanted to let me know she worked there and also wanted to know what I was looking for and for what type of project. I wasn't there to tell my story, which she tried to surreptitiously get from me; although I was sort of curious about hers as I stood there looking at her. I was concerned that she could even begin to help me. There is something peculiar about a person standing in front of you that looks like Mimi Bobeck from the Drew Cary show, blue eye shadow, chunk jewelry, a white stretch scoop top doing more than its intended job with the black bra and all, who wants to help you interior design a home. At least for me, I see this as a business where you're generally serving people who don't have a vision, people that need you to tell and show them how it is done, creating a sense of style that's exciting for the client, not the other way around.

I knew the situation was going to go nowhere fast. Picture this and you'll know why. Here I am standing in a high-end design center, and the designer who is trying to help me has decided to sit down in the barcalounger behind her to talk to me while I am standing. She is in sensible-heeled shoes, like the ones they sell on late night infomercials; they're the style they claim you can work in all day and also play a game of basketball in during your lunch break, so why was she sitting? Her hair was bright blonde, which created a nice contrast to her large scarf she creatively wrapped around her like a tangled parachute or a bad living room drapery swag. She made it disappear behind her and then reappear at the perfect length in front of her, hanging over her right arm just missing the floor. I thought that was creative, but I also thought it must be tiring holding that up all day as if carrying a flag to a flag ceremony with only one free hand to show me anything.

But I could have probably worked around all of that if it wasn't for the perfume. It was the bomb. And that's not slang for meaning good, it was just the opposite, throwing me into a huge allergy attack. Not stopping there the continual waft of it ricocheted up my nose and between my eyes so fast I felt like my head split in two. I can't quite describe it other than it was definitely layered, possibly a body cream topped off with a splash and a spray. She was like a commercial grade lavatory room spritzer but she talked and was in heels. What was she trying to cover up? It was all so overwhelming I started to get stressed, and I knew I had to take the showroom walk on my own. I thanked her and left, realizing the Internet was going to be my first shopping destination.

When I got back to my office, the mail had just been delivered. It was the day when it seems all the magazines and catalogues come at once. Those are usually the days when junk mail isn't my friend, but not that day. I was excited; the timing couldn't have been more perfect. All of the new collections for the season were just coming out, and believe it or not, most of the design houses were showing interiors with a relaxed European flair, just what I wanted. Page after page I was able to tear out of the catalogues creating my storyboard for each room. It was all coming together easier than I had thought, although it did take me about eight months to design, locate, buy and receive all of my merchandise. At the same time I had to find a staging and storage place for everything to go. So I hired a repackaging and freight forwarding company who allowed me to have the merchandise shipped directly to them. They rented me a staging warehouse space where I could unpack, inspect, and organize everything before getting it ready to go into the container.

This was very important so that if anything was damaged, we would find out here and not when it arrived in Italy, since at that point there would be no way for us to make exchanges. Luckily deliveries were scheduled all around the same time to the warehouse, which made our days a lot more efficient.

As the delivery trucks started pulling into the loading docks and we started unloading the boxes, I was shocked at just how much had been purchased. It was my first time seeing it all together in one spot, and I was secretly feeling like I was one of those hoarders they talk about on cable television. So worried I said a quick prayer asking God to please never let that happen to me. While the trucks were being off-loaded, there was a team of people opening and inspecting all the boxes. It's sort of weird looking for something that you really don't want to find. I'm referring to damaged or broken merchandise, which was unfortunately what we were finding. It all very quickly started to feel like a bad Beverly Hills garage sale, and Marie knew I was upset, so she started separating all the damaged merchandise to a different area of the warehouse. We then inventoried it against what had arrived versus what hadn't arrived, and then all damaged merchandise was returned for replacement and then tracked back again. We both felt like we were squares being spun in the middle of a huge rubrics cube!

After several months of sorting, returning, repackaging, labeling, and doing inventory we were ready to start filling the container we had reserved for the shipment. I had reserved only one forty- foot shipping container as I thought that would be sufficient. I've seen them on trains and ships before, so I thought I could judge the size correctly. But no matter how we packed everything and repacked everything, one container was not enough. Two containers were not enough. It actually ended up taking two and a half forty-foot containers to get everything in. Including the inspired fountain I had made for the soon-to-be-courtyard converted parking pad. It was a statue of a woman carrying several baskets of grapes from which the water flowed. It was beautiful, looking as if she was walking through a vineyard with her dress blowing in the wind. I had a special-aged green patina paint mixed and applied to the fountain, making it look historic and weathered, creating the perfect contrast against the yellow stucco background of the villa. I was excited about designing this courtyard space as it would add a real element of beauty and heat relief from the sun that reflected in the summer months off of the cobblestone patio/parking pad at the villa's main entrance. But my plans for that were soon to be interrupted by an "official Italian." I'll tell you more about that later.

With everything packed and secured, the semi-trucks rolled in and picked up the containers. My options were to ship the containers from the West Coast, which would mean they would have to go through the Panama Canal then all the way around the continent to the Atlantic then on to Italy. Or I could send them by train from the West Coast to the East Coast, have them off-loaded onto a container ship on the East Coast, and then shipped across the Atlantic to Italy. Choosing the second option was best as it would save me over a month in shipping time while giving me more leeway on my schedule for possible unforeseen freight forwarding or customs delays. So off the containers went to the train station, not to be seen again until I got to Italy. Was this all going to happen as planned I thought? Would it all be successful? I have heard stories about containers falling off into the ocean never to be seen again or merchandise being pilfered at customs docks. I couldn't bear the thought of any of that; I had to pray for the best.

The month and a half it took for shipping felt like nine months. I seemed to think about it every day, almost like having a baby I guess. You know it's arriving; you plan for the arrival and put so much work into getting everything ready hoping all will go according to plan. You even invite friends to help you with the delivery, as I did. Okay, well maybe you don't go that far for your baby delivery, although I have heard, no I won't go into that. I will just say I was very excited the closer the day got to hearing the phone ring with a call from the shipping broker calling to tell me the shipment had arrived in Italy safe and secure.

Once the call came in confirming everything had arrived, I thought it would be a good idea to invite a couple of my friends to fly over with me to Italy and join in the fun of installing furniture into the villa, and once done, take some side trips, you know, some excursions just because. So I called my good friend Michael and my other friend Jackie. Michael has worked hard his whole life and is single and set. He is always up for an adventure and pretty much enjoys life to the fullest. I told him I was also going to invite my friend Jackie. He knew her through me, and we all got along really great, having dinners and pool parties frequently at her mansion with a lot of wealthy couples scattered around with your garden-variety of wealthy divorced single women; we knew she could be a lot of fun.

Jackie was freshly divorced, or I should say she had kicked out her husband Tom for cheating on her and was in the throes of a huge litigation. She wanted to get away from it all any chance she could and was approaching life the way most very wealthy middle-aged divorcées do, faster than a Wonder Woman spin transformation. Her mostly menopausal monochromatic knit suits turned to miniskirts, tank tops, extra high heels, lots of jewelry, and big hair—she was ready to let the world know "I'm a single woman and ready to have fun!"

Jackie and I had become friends over the last several years through an odd and somewhat uncomfortable set of circumstances. I had casually known her and Tom socially and knew they had been granted the stroke of luck by being involved in the early stages of a global technology company in the Simi Valley but in his case he must have thought it was called *Semen Valley*. It was unfortunate they had just not been so lucky with each other. He decided to start having multiple affairs on her, and I ended up finding out before she did. I always thought she knew something more was up besides her husband, although she never seemed to let on. Through a set of circumstances I was put in a situation where I had to tell her what I knew, which was way too much of what I wish I had never known, but since I knew, I told her everything. It was very uncomfortable, but I felt I was helping her and doing the right thing, as I would probably want someone to do for me. From that moment on she started contacting me more and more often, and we developed a close friendship, I thought. She would tell me over and over I was just like a brother to her and how much she appreciated me. I on the other hand have a wonderful sister already and don't want another. I started including her more and more into my life with my friends and social activities as I felt she was sad and lonely and needed to feel safe with some genuine excitement and friendship in her life. Since she had established upfront that I was apparently like a brother to her, I never thought romance would or could ever be in the picture.

She would tell me stories about what was going on in her divorce, and I felt like she pretty much wanted to keep me in lock step with the proceedings to a certain degree, although

I didn't really care. I knew that's what friends are supposed to do: listen, right? But some of the things she would tell me were shocking, like when she poured honey all over Tom's suits and sweaters that had been stored in a cedar closet, leaving Tom to believe it was cedar sap. He didn't realize he was the only sap in the closet. She then went outside and peed on them after throwing all of his clothes out her balcony doors onto the driveway. For some reason I don't have the image of drip irrigation, but more of Pioneer Midwest sprinkler on the fan spray setting. This all happened the night she was enraged after catching him in a hot and heavy tryst with another woman. As the saying goes, "Hell hath no fury like a woman scorned."

As her story goes, she had been experiencing bouts of "women's intuition" the night after I told her Tom was having an affair with a beach blonde, a blue-eyed, fair-skinned, 'beach' blonde woman in Southern California. Nothing against blondes, but this was a huge switch for Tom as Jackie had coal black hair she wore in an "I just woke up" style and was usually sporting a heavily moisturized deep tan. Jackie ended up acting on her intuition of needing to drive up to the mountains to check on their other home, a five-thousand-square-foot winter cabin retreat, not the home of treats, or so she thought. It was a nice warm summer evening for a top-down drive in her white Aston Martin convertible. She called her next-door neighbor Ping Lie, who also had a cheating husband that she couldn't stand but never divorced because their finances and businesses were too intertwined. Anyway, Jackie asked her to come along for the evening drive. Ping Lie was short and round and always wore flip flops, and although she looked like a cookie jar with feet, she could be tough. Let me just tell you this. One of her businesses was as a consultant who periodically threw in home multilevel marketing parties for a business that rhymes with Tupperware but is called Fu——ware. Now if that's not a pent-up and sexually angry person, I don't know what is. Anyway, Ping Pong, as we called her, was definitely up for the drive. Big surprise as this could be her jackpot night; taking out her aggressions on someone else's cheating man. So into the car they got, putting down the top and seatbelts on. They were now positioned perfectly for an air-through-the-hair hour drive to the cabin, hoping to have their "women's intuition" pay off.

While approaching the last turn onto the main street in front of the cabin, they finalized their just-in-case spy plan.

Quietly rolling up the street in the car, they turned off their lights. The shock of Jackie's life was actually happening before her eyes. Tom's car was parked in the driveway. What was so shocking about that was he had told her he was in California for a business trip, so his car should have been parked at the airport. Let's agree to establish him as an idiot right now. So Ping and Jackie quietly parked the car across the street, got out, and hid in the hedge so they could get a perfect wide span view of the property and house.

Now I'm sure it wasn't hard for Ping to disappear into the four foot hedge, but Jackie, no way. She was at least 5'8", and with her hair pile she had to be a solid 6'. At best even on her knees she would be the height of an average garden hedge with a protruding head having to thank God for her black hair that helped her disappear into the evening sky. Only minutes passed before they had their first sighting, moving shadows and silhouettes behind the half closed drapes of the floor-to-ceiling windows in the living room. As Ping and Jackie slowly moved behind the hedge a little further up the street, they got the perfect angle into the room. And there they saw it, Tom walking naked back into the living room with two glasses of wine. He sat one of them down onto the coffee table and handed the other to someone else, the full moon was definitely out. Then all of a sudden Tom disappeared as a set of women's legs in a pair of hot pink platform heels flew up in the air. Jackie went into a rage and jumped the hedge, Ping's stretch pants got caught as she was jumping out of the hedge yelling at Jackie, but Jackie kept running toward the house. Ping finally unhooked herself ripping out part of the waist band along with a huge hole in her pants, but she didn't care. She was living her fantasy.

Jackie was out of her mind, picking up a piece of wood from the winter wood pile under the deck as Ping caught up to her. Ping tried to convince Jackie not to use wood, but Jackie didn't listen. Running up the stairs onto the deck, Jackie started beating in the back kitchen door, breaking out the windows. Ping jumped up in the air doing a flying double side kick with a jump reverse hook, knocking down the door, giving them full view of Tom running naked through the kitchen. In Jackie's rage, she tried to hit Tom in the head with the wood but he ducked just in time and hit his head on the cabinet door he left open when he got the wine glasses, cutting open his face as the girlfriend ran past and down the hall naked, still in her pink heels. Ping saw that and took off after her. The woman was heading for the master bedroom to get her clothes, but she heard Ping yelling at her, "Get back here you…!" So instead of grabbing her clothes, she tried to crawl under the bed. Right then Ping turned the corner into the room and saw her trying to pull her legs under the bed, like the wicked witch of the east when caught under the falling house. Ping dive bombed her, grabbed her legs and pulled her back out on the floor into the middle of the room. Who knew Ping had a black belt in taekwondo as she ripped off the rest of her waist band and tied up the girlfriend's hands behind her back. Leaving her there in the bedroom she ran back in the kitchen in her ripped-out pants where she heard Jackie screaming at Tom. Tom looked dazed and confused. Ping started yelling at both of them to shut up and call 911 to get an ambulance for Tom. She expected he needed medical help, and the bimbo in the bedroom wouldn't be able to place the call as her hands were tied, literally.

Ping grabbed Jackie and pulled her out of the house to the car while she was still yelling at Tom. As they sped off onto the freeway, Ping asked Jackie if she would mind stopping to get something to eat or maybe a drink. "Are you kidding?" Jackie said as she looked at Ping sitting there half naked in what was left of her pants and spaghetti thong. I guess the cookie jar needed to be filled after using her black belt, I thought, or should I say black waist band from her Kung Fu stretch pants.

Within hours Jackie had all the door locks and gate codes reprogrammed on their mansion, all investment account passwords changed and bank accounts swept. She was out for war, and Ping was finally able to take her aggressions out using her years of training to become a black belt master. I knew Jackie's litigation had the potential to be a long-drawn-out process, so getting her away for a European vacation in the midst of all the commotion would be a good thing for her, or so I thought.

Jackie was excited when I called to ask her. She was doubly excited when she found out Michael was also in. She immediately wanted to plan a dinner at her house for the three of us to discuss the trip, talk about all the things she thought would be fun to see and do that she never had the chance to do with her estranged husband, because as we established before, he was a complete idiot and never knew how to treat her right even on a vacation.

The next night I met Michael and her for dinner at her house. We had a great time talking, laughing, and planning the trip. She told me that night she would like me to go shopping with her the next day if possible. She wanted help picking out a couple of things for the trip at the big Neiman Marcus sale. I never realized she liked to chase down a sale, but more power to her. I, of course, said yes. Before leaving her house that night I excused myself to the restroom and upon my return as I walked down the long hallway back into the kitchen where we had all been talking, I noticed an unusually large oil painting of a scantily clad beach blonde woman in an overly ornate frame hanging on the wall, center court. I don't know why I had never really noticed it before, but this time I did. It was one of those paintings that looked like it could have been anyone, like some of those portraits on canvas paintings they sell once a year in the parking lot under the tent at the home improvement stores. But there were other parts to it that looked too distinctive, such as the diamond necklace she was wearing.

My curiosity got the best of me, so I went in the kitchen and asked Jackie who the person was in the large painting in the hallway. She said it was just a painting that Tom liked on one of their trips to the Taos New Mexico Fall Arts Festival. She said they paid twenty five thousand dollars for it and that he really liked it, so she went along with it. I asked her and Michael to come into the hallway for a minute. I then asked her to really look at that painting, and her mouth dropped. She let out a loud gasp; it was the woman in the pink platform heels. She had been in their house for over two years, looking at her from the hallway while obviously fulfilling one of Tom's sick fantasies. "Oh my god!" she said. "Get her down!"

Michael looked at me and asked, "Do you think we have to be careful with it?"

The next day I met Jackie at Neiman Marcus. She had arrived a little before me to put a few dresses on hold that she wanted me to look at on her once I arrived. We grabbed a quick lunch as she talked to me about the new dresses she wanted to get for herself just in case she, Michael, and I went to a few fancy dinners in Paris or Rome. I said I thought it was a great idea. I also know that shopping helps women to feel better during a crisis, so let the shopping begin. I was a little uncomfortable sitting in the women's department next to the dressing room with another woman walking back and forth to the dressing room looking at me like I was some sort of sick person who was waiting for the right moment to jump in the dressing room with her. So each time Jackie came out and stood in the three-way mirror to talk to me about a dress, I would feel a little more at ease hoping the other woman would see that I was actually there with someone. After the fifth or sixth wardrobe change, no one else was around, except of course for Jeffrey, the assistant who was trying to act invisible unless we needed help. But he was so thin it wasn't hard for him to disappear; one turn around the clothing rounder and he was gone. Like everyone else in "Needless Markup," they're gone, no one is ever there.

Meanwhile, Jackie was coming out in the last dress, one she really liked. She said she saved the best for last. I was excited to see it. As she walked out she was holding up the front top half of the dress, she said she needed help zipping it up. I called the happy male attendant over to assist her. I thought it's safe with him since he would probably enjoy helping Jackie with the dress in a different way, and as for me, well I didn't want to zip her skin up in the dress, so I left it to a "professional." He told her that she first had to put her arm through the hole on the side, she didn't realize there was a hole, or at the very least where it was. And before

Jeffrey could secure the dress from falling, she let go of the top thinking only about getting her arm in the hole. The top fell down, the B-52's dropped out, the dress fell off, and Jeffrey the assistant almost fell like the dress and collapsed while screaming. He spun into a panic and ran behind the clothing rounder he had just come out of.

As for Jackie, all as I could see was her standing there naked in the three-way mirror; my eyes went where they shouldn't. I was frozen in shock as I saw an image that is still seared into my mind, what looked like a hairless Chihuahua caught between her legs with the shine of fresh waxed linoleum. It's all okay though; I just can't talk about the subject as I'm still working on what psychiatrist call "mental imaging removal." It's taken me several years. But here is what was really weird, she was so calm; it didn't seem to faze her at all. In fact, it seemed almost like a planned wardrobe malfunction. But why? I thought I was like a brother to her. What was she doing? Was that what she meant by saving the best for last? If it was her intention, she obviously wasn't aware that it was not a good thing to do, especially when your "situation" looks like a grenade coming at you in a three-way mirror. I honestly felt like I was in a bad funhouse at the county fair, and I wanted out. Once it was all over and she pulled up the dress, Jeffrey reappeared and everyone could breathe normal again. We went ahead and bought a few of the dresses; he felt like he did his job, whatever that was; and I acted like nothing ever happened as I wasn't sure if anything actually had, although I was starting to feel like there was possibly more to her than I had imagined or known. But I didn't want to think the worst, I wanted to trust her intentions, I wanted to feel safe with her agenda, if there was one. Although a person can never know another person's honest intentions or agenda until time is let in to be a part of the equation. So I decided to throw caution to the wind and just have a good time.

One late evening several days later, I got a panicked call from Jackie; she left me a message to please call her back as soon as possible. She sounded very upset, and of course, I thought something bad had happened in her litigation proceedings. I quickly called her back, and to my entire surprise it turned out to be a completely different conversation than I had expected. Several months ago unbeknownst to me, Samuele had called my brother to tell him he had been asked by the Miss Italia World Pageant headquarters in Italy to be part of the selection committee for choosing the next Miss

Italia USA. The chosen contestant would then go on to compete in the Miss Italia World Pageant in Italy. He wanted to know if my brother's oldest daughter Natasha would be interested. The contestant only had to be one quarter Italian to compete, and my niece was half Italian, so it could work. But as it turned out, my niece was not interested in pageantry or being a "pagentrist" for that matter; although I am sure she would have won hands down.

So my brother had to tell Samuele she wasn't interested but that he did have someone else in mind, Jackie's niece Nicole. Personally I didn't see Nicole as pageantry material although she was a cute girl. She was a little on the short side and looked more like a girl you would see modeling trashy lingerie in a mail order catalogue and wonder what went wrong. I think that's why she came to live with Jackie so Jackie could help her get straightened out. She also didn't wear her hair correctly for her face; she needed a hairstyle with twenty-four hour bangs since she had unfortunately inherited a five head from someone in her gene pool, which I think was her incarcerated father. The rule of thumb for good facial symmetry is you should never be able to fit more than four fingers horizontal between your eyebrows and your hair line; hence the term forehead was created for a reason. If you can fit five, then you have a five head, and so on. The bottom line is anything over four can be severely distracting to look at, and she was teetering between a five and a six. The one time in life I can think of when a girl does not want to be referred to as a ten.

I don't know what Mark was actually thinking or if he really was, but in any event, Mark went on to tell Samuele the backstory of Jackie and how this could be the perfect situation for her niece and that the three of them should meet. Samuele was interested; of course, he then asked Mark if he would set up a meeting for them at his restaurant. So Mark texted Jackie, told her what was up; and Jackie immediately replied back that Nicole was interested, and yes they would go to Samuele's restaurant to meet him, so please set up the meeting. In a matter of minutes Mark had made an introduction with everyone on a group text, and Samuele had set up a time to meet them. Now I don't know about you, but if I were told I had an interview scheduled for my niece with the head judge of the Miss Italia America pageant, that is one thing; and when I found out it would be at his Italian restaurant that is another thing. But when I find out the pageant will be taking place at his gelateria next door called Che cosa è lo scoop?, a.k.a. "What's the Scoop?" then that should cause anyone in their right mind to start having a different conversation with their own intuition. At least it would me, but apparently that didn't happen. Jackie went ahead and showed up with Nicole, push up bra, thigh highs, and heels ready to be chosen. Or so she thought. She went on to tell me that she and her niece Nicole showed up at Samuele's fine dining restaurant, Pomodoro di Oro ("The Golden Tomato"), that night so they could have dinner and then he could meet her and Nicole and talk with them both about Nicole being in the preliminary local pageant before she left town for an internship she had coming up in New York. Time seemed to be of the essence, and everything seemed very last minute and rushed, which should have been another red flag.

As in many authentic Italian restaurants, the owner usually makes his way around the restaurant to talk and add a personal touch to the patrons' experience, but in this case Samuele's touch became too personal. He introduced himself when they showed up and told them once they were done with dinner he would come over and talk with them, which is what happened. Samuele knew right away when he saw

Nicole that it wasn't going to work out, for the same reasons that I had mentioned above, but he was nice and had her fill out the required application and attach a picture of her for him. But what Samuele did decide would work out was Jackie, he thought she would be a perfect candidate for him. After the interview he told Jackie if she wanted to get together at some point in the very near future to discuss all the details with him that Nicole didn't need to be bothered with, then that would be a good idea. He then got up from the table and said he would be right back.

Jackie thought it would be a good idea to stay and have the conversation with Samuele that night while they had his interest, so she told Nicole to drive her car home and that she would call her when she needed to be picked up. When Samuele came back, Nicole was gone, and Jackie was sitting there alone with her glass of wine. Samuele asked where Nicole was. Jackie explained and at that moment Samuele's "peter meter" took over. He went and got two new wine glasses, two bottles of wine, sat down and started to tell Jackie he was finally going through with his long awaited decision of getting a divorce. As the evening progressed he proceeded to tell Jackie that he wanted to date her and that she was the most beautiful woman he had ever seen. It was now close to 11:00 p.m., and everyone had left the restaurant leaving just the two of them. He went on to tell her they could have a wonderful life together, and he could really make her happy. How could he know this, he has only known her for a few hours? I'm thinking, this had to be the wine talking.

She then told me she was shocked and disgusted. She said she got up to leave, and he grabbed her, planted a deep kiss on her mouth while pushing himself into her with what felt like an Italian link sausage from the kitchen against her leg. When he realized she wasn't responding and was pulling back, he handed her a bill for the evening's dinner and drinks. *Was this the real "Golden Tomato"?* I thought while I listened in shock.

I told her not to worry. I had heard he had a pattern of doing this with women and that he just probably had too much to drink. She then asked me if he was going to be in Europe at the villa while we were there. She didn't want him anywhere around. She must have had a premonition or knew something I didn't. I told her no, he would not be there. I then called Michael and woke him up to tell him the story. He couldn't believe it and then also told me I needed to make sure Samuele is not anywhere around while we are in Italy, that it would be a really bad idea since Jackie was going to be there with us. *Why were they both telling me this?* I thought as I assured Michael he would not be there and this was going to be just a trip for the three of us.

Michael, Jackie, and I went ahead and finalized all our travel plans, made the reservations, and were set to go. I also called my brother and sister-in-law who were in Paris at the time and told them what had happened to Jackie. They said not to worry, but there was a chance Samuele could be in Italy when we all are there. Mark had told Samuele the three of us were coming to meet him and Marie at the villa to do the furniture installation, which I still don't know why he did that.

Anyway, Samuele then told Mark he would also try to make it over if he could. Samuele thought it would be a good idea if he could help us with the move-in and interpret for us with the movers. I didn't know what to do; I knew Jackie was going to be very upset if that was to end up happening. I told Mark to tell Samuele not to come. If I needed help interpreting, I would hire an interpreter; it wasn't worth the potential drama if he were to show up.

Knowing there were still a couple of weeks before we were going to leave, I decided to go online and search for anything fun and exciting I could plan as a surprise for Michael and Jackie, sort of as a thank-you for all of the help they were going to give me. I had heard there was an exclusive tour that could be taken in Rome called the Scavi. This was an underground tour below the Vatican at the tomb of St. Peter and the Necropolis. This tour was granted only through a special application approval process by the Fabbrica di San Pietro at the Vatican with the appointment times set by the Office of Excavations. Thinking this could be a very special surprise few people in the world would ever be able to do, I set out to write a letter to the Vatican's official office that handles the approval. I told them I was traveling to Rome with two of my very good friends, one of my friends is American Orthodox Christian and the other is Catholic. I explained that I was raised Protestant (which I've been told supposedly stands for protester of the original faith). I also told them that I was on a quest into a deeper study of what both of my friends believed. Was I actually unknowingly a protester from the original faith (Orthodox), or were the Catholics the first protesters and the Protestants second? And was that part of the Great Schism in the Church? It was all so confusing for me. I had so many questions that needed answers.

I went on to write that if given the chance to take this tour, I was sure many of my questions would be answered. So I guess in some ways it was like a pilgrimage for me.

Within seven days I received an e-mail back from the Office of Excavations. They had approved the request, and we had a letter of confirmation for the three of us. I was very excited. This was going to be an experience of a lifetime.

In the letter they outlined the following information: Arrive at the Excavations Office at least ten minutes before the scheduled time of the visit. Clothing should be appropriate for a sacred place. Long trousers, slacks, jeans for men; dresses that reach below the knees or long trousers, slacks, jeans for women. Shoulders must be covered for all. Entrance to the Excavations Office is only through the gates located on the Via Paolo VI (outside of the colonnade, just to the south (left), near the entrance to the General Audience Hall.) Upon arrival, present the Swiss Guards with your letter of confirmation received from the office, which indicates the scheduled time of your visit. Wow, I thought this is really going to be exciting. It's all so official and somewhat mysterious, with Swiss Guards and all.

CHAPTER 5

Up, Up and Away

I hardly slept the night before our departure, I had a lot to do in the morning and I was scared I would over sleep then wouldn't have a chance for finishing last minute things or that our driver and town car would not show up. So I set my alarm early enough for the just in case. Fortunately everything worked out; the driver was at my home at 11:30 just as scheduled, helped load my bags, and off we went to pick up Jackie. Now I like to travel sensibly, putting everything into nondescript luggage, in this case a rolling carry-on that fits in the overhead compartment of the plane. I also carry a backpack that secures to the top of the rolling bag, that way I have an easy access bag for my travel documents, reading material, and basic travel necessities; this then doubles as an excursion bag for side trips from my main travel destinations. And the best part of traveling this way is no waiting in baggage claim lines and no chance of luggage getting lost. Once we arrived at Jackie's I rang the intercom at the gate to tell her we were there. She buzzed the gate open and asked if we could come in quickly and help her with her luggage.

Several days earlier Michael, Jackie, and I had a discussion on how to pack, and we all agreed to pack the same way. So I didn't understand why her entryway was stacked with two large brown herculon and leather Hartman rolling wardrobes, an oversized back-breaking Louis Vuitton bucket bag, and a random mid-size travel case that actually could fit in the overhead. Maybe she got confused, or better yet, maybe she thought as long as she had the overhead bag and the carry-on she had complied with our agreed packing arrangements. I sort of just stood there with a racing mind, not even wanting to ask why. So with a good morning hug, kiss, and smile on my face, we loaded the town car, which by now looked like a caravan, and off we drove. When we arrived at the airport Jackie handed several large bills to the driver and asked if he could assist with taking her bags to the check-in counter. Of course he said no problem. As he rolled her wardrobes down the ramp toward the counter, she followed closely behind looking like a pack mule. A carry-on bag in one hand, the Louis Vuitton bucket bag over her shoulder, and a phone in the other hand, oh and I forgot to mention, she was covered in jewelry. The centerpiece was a huge diamond studded cross that hung from her neck on a thick gold braded rope diving into her cleavage, gold bangle bracelets in every size up her right arm, with the "just a little too loose" diamond Rolex that rolled around on her left arm. And for the rings, well of course the wedding finger was freed up, but the right hand had on the statement ring, a fire opal the size of a quail egg surrounded by diamonds on her index finger.

I knew all this was going to send Michael into a tail spin, not to mention potentially create the TSA nightmare he vehemently tries to avoid. So I purposefully lagged a little behind, just until Michael saw us coming in, I wanted her to be at the head of the parade. Sure enough right then we caught his eyes, his face dropped, and all I could see was his mouth moving to words that looked like, "Oh my god, are you kidding me!" Luckily she didn't see him say that as she approached him with her good-morning two-cheek faux Italian kiss. I was laughing, he was mad and trying to hide it, and Jackie, well, she didn't know any better. She just stood there looking around puffing up her hair trying to make it bigger.

The closer we got to the TSA line, the more nervous I got. Why? Because I knew there was going to be a situation. There had to be. Jackie was with us, and so were her carry-ons and jewelry. Jackie was next in line, and the lady was trying to direct her into the scanning chamber, but Jackie refused to use it. She said she didn't want a random person being able to look through her clothes at her body on a big black-and-white screen. I asked her if it would make a difference if it was in color; she didn't think that was funny. I actually think the reason is different than that. I think she doesn't want to lose her hair. I know I wouldn't. I mean think about it. Have you ever seen anyone operating those machines that have a full head of hair? Never, they are always bald or a few hairs from it. So Jackie opted out and went into the "special line". Michael and I also opted out, but we had to go into a different line because the "assist" as they call it can only be the same sex as the person opting out. I think Jackie was disappointed when she finally figured that out. Michael and I got through quickly, put on our belts and shoes and waited at the other end watching Jackie get the wand. By this time she had all of her jewelry off, her shoes off, and a metal sparkly hair clip off, but she was still setting off the wand. I could tell by the look on her face when she had opted for the wand, she had been expecting a little nicer wand with all the options. We could hear the lady telling her to turn around and put her hands in the air, almost like she was in jail; she was going to do one more sweep. If she didn't pass, they would then have to step into the tent for a private showing.

I could also tell Jackie was irritated, first because she didn't have a man giving her the "wand," and second because she felt she had emptied herself of everything, other than the oatmeal she had for breakfast. Then lo and behold, as Jackie's arms went up in the air, her white cotton top went up too, and the prize fell out, literally. A five carat diamond stud she had double pierced through her bellybutton that she said she had forgot about. I don't think so. You couldn't forget about something like that. It was more than a belly button bling; I would say it looked more like her private door knocker for special visitors. I thought to myself this is ridiculous. Is anyone really home?

At that point Michael was on the edge with her; I could just feel it. And even though we still had an hour before we had to board the plane, he wanted to get to the gate, confirm our check-in and seating, then get a coffee. We all agreed that would be the best thing to do, and good thing we did because they decided to board the plane thirty minutes early, and the plane was full. It is right at that point when you arrive at the gate and you see the huge crowd of people getting ready to board that you thank God you are turning "left." I always say I like to turn left because that's usually what you do when you get to fly first or business class: you enter the cabin and turn left, and on this trip we were fortunate enough to be able to do that. Once we got on I was happy to see the seats were large padded leather and reclined with full leg rests. The cabin was a two, two-and-two configuration. We were on the right side of the plane; and I had a window seat and was sitting directly in front of Michael and Jackie. As we got all situated, bags overhead, lumbar pillow blown up, blankets stowed, Michael tapped my seat to make sure I had seen the travel amenity kit in the side pocket. It was a kit created by the luggage company Tumi and featured a virtually abrasion-proof ballistic nylon fabric case, seemed a little overboard to me, but nice. It was stocked with all natural goodies from the apothecary Malin + Goetz. There was Neroli hand and body lotion and lip moisturizer, Tumi eye mask, earplugs, toothbrush and paste, and of course plush travel socks. And everything but the eye mask and socks were in cute little hobbit sizes.

Once the final cabin check was done, it seemed only to be minutes and we were airborne. We couldn't believe it; we were on our way. As we settled in the flight attendants started giving us drinks and snacks while they took our dinner orders. The next thing we knew the lights in the cabin started to dim as the crew subtly tried to start pushing the passengers onto a European schedule. I put on my headset, turned on my music, reclined my seat, and started to relax. Several hours later after falling into a relaxed light sleep I was awoken by the flight attendant who wanted to take my drink order to go with my dinner. I didn't even remember falling asleep, I thought, as I ordered a large glass of ice water. Realizing I was really thirsty while my skin was feeling dry, I decided to go to the restroom in the back of the business class cabin to wash my hands before dinner and put some of the Neroli body lotion on my face. Unfortunately for me and possibly others, the brainiac that designed the contents of the travel case didn't clearly delineate between the toothpaste tube and the skin lotion tube. I grabbed the wrong one to take with me to the restroom, and I proceeded to cover my face in tooth-paste. I thought it seemed a little thick and minty smelling, but I was too caught up in the idea of imagining it to be some sort of European version of what I had used in the past, so I just went with it. After it was all rubbed into my face it really started to burn, my face was turning bright red and the mint vapors were burning my eyes. Immediately knowing some-thing was wrong, I looked at the tube again but the writing was so small I couldn't read it without my reading glasses, and I had left those in the seat pocket in front of me. I then knew what I had done. What an idiot! I thought to myself. Are you kidding me?

I tried to start rinsing off my face, but every time I pressed down the water lever, the water would come out for five seconds, the water lever would go up, and the water would go off. The burning was getting worse so with my left hand I held down the lever and cupped my right hand to fill with water and started to splash my face. Not only was the toothpaste concentrated, making the mint burn more with water, but it also started to foam, and by now it was get-ting worse. So I soaked a wad of paper towels with water and squeezed them out onto my face over the playhouse sink while wiping my face at the same time. After several minutes of doing this and all but flooding the restroom, I finally got it all off, but my shirt was drenched, my face was burned, and the restroom had water everywhere. I wasn't even about to start wiping down the walls, the toilet, and the floor. In fact I almost started to gag just thinking about it, not to mention I was mad the airline would allow those tubes not to be clearly marked. Why was every tube white and black? How about throwing in a green tube for minty toothpaste, or better yet, how about red to match your skin once you've rubbed it in! As I opened the door and walked out to find a flight attendant to alert about the condition of the restroom, I pulled back the curtain, knowing that's where they usually congregate in a gossip huddle, and standing right there was Samuele. Had the vapors burned my eyes? Was that really him I was seeing? In shock I blurted out, "Is that really you?"

"Surprise," he said. "So good to see you, Baaabe, where are you sitting?" My stomach sank, my mind started to race, and as all as I could think was *Oh my god! Now what!* as he grabbed me and gave me a big hug. By this time I not only had a wet shirt and burned face but was also now wearing his catalogue-only cologne that had rubbed off on me. It was the kind that jumps onto your clothes from another person with something as simple as a quick hug. How could my life been so altered so fast? What were Michael and Jackie going to do, how do I handle this? Then I realized I needed to jump in and share the load as this shouldn't just be my problem to burden. So I looked him right in the eye with a smile and said follow me. When we walked up behind Michael and Jackie, I could see they had already been served their wine and were eating their dinner, not knowing I was bringing them dessert. "Hey you guys, look who's here," I said as I walked up the aisle next to them. Jackie looked up in shock, Michael almost choked on his wine as I continued to my seat with my wet cologned shirt and red face. Leaving them with Samuele I laughed to myself thinking things really do happen in threes, and no matter how hard you try there are those times where there is just nothing you can do about it.

The flight attendants suddenly appeared in the aisles again and told Samuele that he had to return to his assigned cabin. Michael handed him a glass of wine for his journey back, which Samuele took as a nice gesture. I saw it more like a departing gift on a game show. I was relieved, but not knowing what to say I didn't turn around to comment; I just ate my dinner and looked busy, but within minutes I heard Jackie going into a panic attack. I then partially turned around to see what was going on as I was being held by my seatbelt. She was frantic, riffling through her Louis Vuitton bucket bag asking Michael if he knew how to do CPR.

"What?" he asked.

"CPR," she said in a panicked voice.

"Yes," he said with a scared look on his face asking, "Why?"

"Because I just realized those were chopped scallops sprinkled on the salad, and I ate them by mistake when Samuele showed up. I told the flight attendant I have a shell fish allergy when she took our order. I told her I couldn't have any shellfish and that my food could not even be prepared next to shell fish, she said no problem, but I knew she wasn't listening. She was too busy staring at you. Hurry; help me find my Epipen! "I can feel my face getting hot and my throat closing." She yelled under her breath, "I could die within twenty minutes, my lips are starting to tingle, and they're going to swell up over my nose, hurry I need my pen!" Michael took the bag and dumped it over onto the seat; a pack of ten Epipens fell out. I quickly turned around to unfasten my seatbelt so I could get out and help. It was all happening so fast, and I was also starting to get scared even though I subconsciously could see nothing happening to her face. I guess I just believed what I was hearing and not what I was seeing. I asked the girl next to me if she could please let me by to see what was going on. She then took off her headset and said, "I'm sorry, what?"

Right then Jackie said to Michael, "Stick it in, hurry don't be scared, just stick it in."

Michael said, "Where?"

"Right there, hurry give it to me fast!" The girl next to me looked at me in horror; I could tell by the look on her face she thought she was overhearing members of the mile-high club. I was embarrassed as she knew I was traveling with them. I told her "It's not what you think…its shell fish." She jumped up, I jumped out and around to the back seat. Michael had just pulled the pen out of her leg, and Jackie was breathing loud and fast. I told them I was going to get the flight attendant. I went to the galley as fast as I could, found the attendant, and asked her to please come back to our seats telling her that my travel companion was just on the verge of going into anaphylactic shock.

"From what?" she said running up the aisle.

"From the chopped shell fish you put on her salad," I said to her in disgust while getting from her what seemed to be a puzzled look on her face. We got to Jackie and Michael's seats, and Michael went on to tell the attendant what had happened and he was mad. "I'm sorry, sir, she said in a controlled calm voice, that was not shell fish, it was chopped macaroni." I really don't know how Michael stayed so calm after he heard that, other than his level of extreme calm was probably the indicator of his extreme disgust. I believed at that moment he and I both thought we had seen it all.

It seemed to be only three to four more hours, and we had landed in Paris for our transfer flight onto Firenze. Where you ask? Oh, I forgot to mention one minor detail. When you get into Paris to make your connection, the name Florence changes to Firenze. I guess everyone is supposed to know that among many other things they don't tell you upon arrival, making it even more difficult to locate your flight. We finally located our flight, and Samuele located us. Together we waited to board; he was very excited to be on the next flight with us and immediately started talking too loud too fast and nonstop becoming our self-appointed travel director. Again, I was sure he meant well, but it was obvious he was excitedly nervous around Jackie, and I was severely lacking sleep. By this time everything was becoming magnified to me, including the thirty-five-dollar cost of the four croissants and four small orange juices I purchased for us at the concession across the walkway from the departure gate—only to see Samuele had already bought himself a glass of wine and was chugging it in the corner. When they finally announced the boarding call, I couldn't wait to get back onto the plane. Looking forward to a first-class seat, I wanted to go to sleep even if it was for just a couple of hours. It was already midmorning, which meant we would be getting into Firenze close to noon. As we boarded the plane the flight attendant asked to see my boarding pass. I showed it to her and told her we were in first class. She said, "Okay, please continue this way to your seat." But I wasn't turning left I thought. I'm turning right, and why are the seats so small? They had sold us first class tickets, and all of the seats were in the same cabin and were two and two's. I got to my seat, which was not much bigger than a jump seat, and couldn't believe this is what we had been charged extra for. With the seat in front of me only inches away, I pushed the attendant button and asked what was going on. She assured me I was in the correct seat and that first class on this flight meant that no one would be sitting next to me. How would that even be possible anyway? I thought as I was sitting in what felt like one seat cut into two. Then a guy the size of a small hairy walrus sat down into the seat directly in front of me. That's all it took to be able to realize my small blessing that he didn't sit down next to me and pour himself over into my seat.

I don't mind at all if someone sits next to me; just be clean and groomed especially for airplane travel where quarters are tight anyway. And I knew if this guy sat next to me he would have one of those sticky hairy arms that would gently graze against my arm like sandpaper every time the plane jerked. It would have unnerved me. Once we took off I laid my seat back, closed my eyes, and tried to let the humming of the jet engines lull me to sleep. When I just started to go into that suspended state of sleep where you know where you are but you don't care if your mouth drops open. We've all seen that before on airplanes, right? We'll, it was just at that point I started to smell something bad, almost like hot bologna and a mildewed gym bag. I gently opened my eyes part way to see if I could locate where it was coming from; the smell seemed to be getting more intense and I was hoping it wasn't something they were going to try and serve us from the food cart. As soon as I completely opened my eyes I saw that the big hairy sweaty guy in front of me had also laid his seat back as far as he could, and his bald spot was right under my nose. Honestly, what was the airline thinking to make the seats this way? Was this supposed to be another first-class perk they don't mention? Like the warm crushed nuts they offer, which I didn't need to take since mine already were. The poor man was obviously nervous flying as his head was profusely sweating; it was even coming through his white shirt like glazing on a donut. My only recourse was to reach above and turn the air dial onto full blast, point it straight down to make an air wall between his head and my nose, making sure there was a slight slant forward with the air dial so any other potential fowl smells would go in that direction, forward. I was happy he didn't say anything about the air hitting him as I sat there staring at the few long hairs he had left on his head flying around in circles, maybe he was a TSA employee who ran the scanners I thought.

We finally landed at Amerigo Vespucci Airport in Firenze, our final destination for the next six days. We gathered our entire luggage load, or should I say Jackie's luggage load and put it onto a cart for our trek outside and over to the car rental area. Since I had been there before, I knew what to do. Samuele said good-bye, did the traditional contrived Italian double cheek kiss, and told us he was staying at his mother's house but would see us later, probably tomorrow after the furniture arrived. I just said "Great," we'll see you tomorrow, thinking right then he had forgotten the furniture was arriving in several hours and not tomorrow. What I should have told him was "Let us give you a call once we are ready."

CHAPTER 6

On What a Night

It was a beautiful day in Tuscany. The air was warm and there was a light breeze. But as I looked out over the countryside, I saw the familiar haze of a hot Tuscan day laying low on the horizon, and I knew the temperature would only be going in one direction, up!

I had called ahead several weeks earlier to Samuele's family, letting them know we were coming just because I thought it would be polite, and also in case someone didn't tell them, like possibly Samuele. I didn't know why, but I had a feeling there could have been a slight chance he didn't say anything. Again, I can't tell you why, but for some reason it was a feeling I had. Samuele's daughter Sofia was in college and living with her relatives in Italy at the time we were going to be there, so I knew she would be able to interpret for me to the family as well as with the movers on the day of the move in. The main reason for my call was to tell Sofia it was extremely important to make sure they move everything out of the villa before we got there. The movers would be showing up in the early afternoon the day of our arrival, and we needed to make sure everything was clean and ready.

When we arrived at the villa and opened the grand wooden doors, I was gently horrified as to what I saw. Room after room were still filled with stuff, and not good stuff, not even secondhand stuff, but more like fifth hand stuff if there's such a thing. There were still the old beds with broken down stained mattresses, hard thin sheets, pillows, blankets, gouged out pressboard wardrobes with missing handles, bad dorm room floor lamps, outdoor yard loungers in the living room, the kind with plastic straps that leave marks on your skin like you've been laying on a grill, and the list goes on.

I am not sure how I could have said we needed everything removed from inside the villa any clearer to Sofia. She speaks fluent English, what was the problem? As all as I can think is somehow the request got lost in translation to the family, and to my fault I had not taken that possibility into consideration.

Knowing we had to work fast and couldn't all stand there in shock looking at all the stuff as if it was going to move itself, we all three went into action. Michael and Jackie said they would take the upstairs, and I took the main floor, since there was more stuff to move upstairs and I needed to watch for the movers. Without wasting any time I called Sofia and asked her if she could please come over right away. I told her that we needed her help, she said no problem she was on her way. Not two minutes after I hung up the phone, I heard noises outside as if something was being hit. I didn't pay much attention at first, but then realizing it was becoming more frequent, I ran outside to check what was happening. Right then two smashed pillows went flying over my head, a cloud of feathers and a bundle of old ripped blankets right behind. As I looked up I saw Jackie heaving an old nasty metal floor lamp over the balcony. Michael and Jackie had actually taken it upon themselves to decide that nothing was worth saving, and they were not going to move junk down the stairs. They determined that all of it must have been left there because nobody wanted it, and the quickest way to clear everything out was to throw it all out the windows into the yard.

I honestly couldn't believe what I was seeing as I ducked for cover having visions of Jackie throwing her husband's stuff out the balcony window of her home. She was in full action, aggressively swinging her whole body to the side while throwing her arms up to the sky and letting everything go, hurling it through the air. By the look on her face she seemed to really be enjoying it in some odd way. Maybe she still had aggressions against her ex-husband she hadn't dealt with yet. I didn't know nor did I really care; I just went back into the kitchen to work and started laughing. I couldn't believe we were in a hot, humid, dirty villa in Italy throwing stuff out of windows, and movers were coming within hours to move in over two forty-foot containers of furniture. Let's also keep in mind the fact that none of us speak the language so we couldn't explain the situation or talk with them when they arrived, and I didn't want to take the risk of having Jackie try and communicate to them with her interpretive dance moves or they may never return with the remainder of the deliveries! We were in a mess!

Thank goodness shortly thereafter Sofia showed up. I met her in what I call the great room, and I asked her what had happened. She asked me the same thing as she looked at the piles of stuff through the opened doors out in the yard. I told her that the movers were coming shortly, and that's why I had called several weeks earlier to make sure all contents were moved out of the villa and everything was thoroughly cleaned, windows, floors, etc. I also told her we thought all the good stuff worth keeping must have been moved out and what was left looked like junk that no one wanted, so we threw it out. She looked at me in shock and went on to tell me that right after I had called her she phoned her dad in the U.S. and told him about our call and asked him why I wanted everything moved out and cleaned out. Samuele told her not to worry about anything, that we were coming for vacation and would be staying at the villa. He went on to tell her I had purchased some great pieces of furniture at a discount and had them sent over to the villa for him. He also told her I would be doing a little decorating while I was there and that he would take care of everything once he arrived.

"Are you kidding me!" I said in disbelief.

"No," she said, "that's exactly what he told me."

"Well," I said, "the little decorating is over two and a half forty-foot shipping containers of furniture and house goods, it's not exactly a little decorating, and by the way, did he say anything about the fact that he sold the villa? Right then Samuele walked in. Sophia ran over yelling at him, "Dad, what is going on?"

"Don't worry, babe," he said, "I made an arrangement, it's not a big deal, so don't worry." I looked at Samuele and told him I wasn't sure what was going on, but I hoped he had remembered over two containers of furniture were expected to show up within the hour. He said he remembered, and that's why he came over to help. Knowing he probably needed to have a conversation with Sophia; I turned around and walked back into the kitchen.

I hadn't been in the kitchen for more than thirty seconds, and I couldn't believe what I was hearing. Jackie was cussing like a sailor and Michael wasn't far behind. What was going on now, I thought, as I ran up the long staircase to make sure they were okay. When I got to the top I remembered that heat rises. It felt familiar, like a wall of heat I had experienced in Tuscany before, but this time it was like a hundred-and-fifty-degree wall of heat that hit me along with the immediate thought that neither of them did their own house cleaning. Jackie has full time staff at her mansion, and Michael, well even though he is a hard worker he also has a maid; in fact, he grew up with one.

I decided it was probably best not to make myself known; so I just peeked around the corner, and there were Jackie and Michael mopping the tile floors with homemade mops. Actually they were long broom sticks with wet rags on the end. They were pushing dirt around with these sticks and rags, back and forth, cussing like prisoners who were finishing out a prison sentence for a crime they never did. I couldn't help but start laughing. Jackie's hair pile had slid to the side of her head with long wet strings of it flopping in her face. Her white pedal pushers were covered in dirt and smudge and the bottoms of her immaculately kept French-pedicured feet were bare and black.

Michael, on the other hand, who usually has a perfectly stacked full head of hair that defies gravity with its height, looked like he was wearing a hot sweaty pancaked toupee in basic black. It was flat to his head and wet around the fringe. His usual perfectly pressed tucked in shirt was wrinkled and untucked hanging on him like a wet sack. I could tell the two of them were mad, exhausted, and couldn't believe what they were doing and why. I didn't have the courage to tell either of them Samuele was downstairs, so I quietly turned around and again went back to the kitchen. Thank God for the kitchen, I was now bookended in drama!

With everything cleaned and cleared out, the villa was ready for its special delivery. Michael and Jackie came downstairs to the kitchen with the serious "don't even ask" looks on their faces. Luckily I had just made a large container of cold and fresh Sorrento lemon lemonade and handed each of them a large chilled glass filled to the top. The three of us sat in folding chairs to rest for a minute since we knew the next event would be starting shortly, but the event was not what any of us were expecting, well not exactly anyway. Hearing vehicles pulling up out front, we thought for sure it was the delivery trucks, only to be shocked that it wasn't. It was the rest of Samuele's family, his emotional mother, his confused-looked brother and sister-in-law Anastasia, still wearing her acrylic heeled leopard pumps, but this time with shorts, a chain belt, and a leather on leopard-trimmed halter top. Maybe she wanted me to know she had tamed the tiger or leopard as it were. They had all seemingly arrived to do the "we just stopped by to say hi" routine. Not planning on helping and definitely not planning on seeing a huge pile of their stuff randomly heaved into the front yard.

As Michael, Jackie and I walked outside to say hi, we saw Samuele standing there with Sofia trying to explain to his mother, brother, and sister in law what he had done. His mother was walking around the pile in circles crying, throwing her hands in the air as if part of a tribal dance while not listening to anything Samuele was trying to say. Again not being able to speak or understand Italian, the three of us just stood there not knowing what to do. It was actually sort of scary so I secretly started praying for the trucks to hurry up and get there so the tension would be dampened or at least interrupted. And as if out of nowhere my prayers were answered. Three small white trucks pulled up, definitely not the semi-trucks I had expected, but more along the size of small wonder bread trucks from the 1960s. Sofia came running over to greet the drivers and figure out the logistics etc. As the trucks started pulling forward I asked her what was going on. Quickly Michael and Jackie came over to join in the huddle with us behind one of the trucks. "Well, first of all," she said, "my dad never told my Nona that he was selling the villa." She went on to tell us that the villa had been left to Samuele at the time of his father's passing. He was going to try and get it fixed up as a family country estate, but it became impossible. It had all become too much for him to try and deal with. All the repairs and remodel after four hundred years, his divorce, and also the fact of him trying to deal with it when he didn't even live in the country anymore—it was all too overwhelming for him. And I could see why as I looked on at his family who had now joined Giada in the walk around the mound also yelling and throwing their hands in the air. It was obvious he was wearing all of it on his shoulders, and he had to make some decisions.

I then went on to ask her why everyone was walking around the pile in the yard yelling, crying, and pulling stuff out. She told us since her dad didn't want to tell the family anything until he got there; they never got the message to clean everything out. I guess his timing was slightly more than a little off. What was thrown out the balcony was actually their stuff and stuff they wanted to keep. "Oh sh———t," Michael and Jackie said at the same time, and for me, well, I didn't even know what to say. I was in shock. I was in disbelief! We all felt horrible, but Sofia was so sweet she pulled her long blonde hair up into a bun and told us not to worry, that she was used to this stuff with her family, and her father would just have to figure it out.

"Let's get to work," she said as I was now starting to understand why wine is the national drink of choice in Italy. With this kind of drama you have to have it within arm's reach at all times, and I could see it in Jackie's eyes, even Michael's for that matter. If they could, they would have sat down right then and there, and each drank a full bottle. And I'm not talking about a baby bottle. "So why the little trucks," I asked Sofia, "don't they have bigger ones?

"They do," she said, "but they can't get through the small streets of the village with big trucks so they have to off-load everything into these small trucks and drive everything in." Of course they do, why not? I thought. This is Italy, and it's going to be a very long day. Fortunately for us, they kept the trucks rolling in, and Sofia was right there directing traffic along with telling everyone in fluent Italian what furniture, what boxes, and what lighting fixtures went into what rooms. I gave her the inventory list Marie had prepared of all of the boxes, which were numbered, each number corresponding to a room on the list for placement.

I was very thankful Marie had the idea to do that as it made everything run so much smoother, which was something we all needed by now. The official move-in was finally happening for real.

Everyone worked extremely hard that day into the early evening. We weren't able to get everything done, but the majority of it was finished with just minor details left for the next day. Sofia offered to go to the grocery store and get some antipasti and wine while everyone else took showers and got ready for a relaxed evening at the villa. It was all really looking beautiful, almost like stepping into a magazine. With the outdoor patio furniture set in place, Jackie offered to prepare the food that Sofia had brought back. She put together large platters of antipasti, fresh bread with olive oil and aged balsamic vinegar, along with perfectly ripened fruit and red wine. I sat out on the patio looking over the vineyards. The sun was setting into a majestic artist's pallet of orange, pink, light blue, and yellow. Of course those colors made me hungry for some authentic Italian gelato, but that would have to wait for another night.

After the dinner was over I found myself sitting there not understanding what anyone was saying or talking about. I must have fallen asleep, and no one noticed. I was exhausted, so I went ahead and excused myself to go to bed while Michael, Jackie, Samuele and several others continued to entertain themselves with wine and good conversation well past midnight. As I lay in my bed with the shutters open to feel the late evening breeze, I could hear all of them below telling jokes, laughing, and having a good time. Great, I thought, maybe things are going to be better between everyone; I can now go to sleep. Several hours later I was awoken from a deep sleep, Samuele and Michael came running into my room yelling, "Randy, where is Jackie? We can't find her anywhere." I woke up not knowing where I was and completely disoriented.

"What do you mean where is Jackie?" I said as I tried to figure out what was going on? "I went to bed hours ago, and you're asking me where she is? When I left the table all of you were together, you should be asking yourselves where she is!" I was starting to get mad, especially once I looked at the clock next to the bed, and it said 3 a.m. "How long has she been gone?" I asked in a panic.

"Probably about an hour," Samuele said. "But we thought she went to bed. We all were just going to bed, and when we walked past her room the door was open, and we saw the bed still made and she wasn't in there."

"This is what happens when people are up way too late drinking way too much wine," I said like an old Italian mother yelling at her kids. I started laughing as I really couldn't believe it again; this had to be the longest night of my life quickly approaching the longest week. We searched the house, every room, every closet, yelling for her, but no answer. Then Michael reminded us that Stella next door had a search and rescue dog she had adopted named Angelo.

"Great," I said, "but it's after three in the morning, Stella is asleep!"

"It doesn't matter," Samuele said. "I can wake her up."

I'm sure you can, I thought. Michael and Samuele went next door to awaken Stella and get Angelo. I ran upstairs to Jackie's room, opened her luggage, and in a hurry grabbed the first thing I saw: a pair of black lace panties. Next to them I saw a Giorgio of Beverly Hills Red Eau de Toilette fragrance gift set. Even though it was brand new, I ripped it open and sprayed down the panties; I knew I had seen this on TV before. You have to give the dog a scent to pick up. I was just hoping this one didn't burn out his nose! Running back down the stairs and out the door, I looked next door and saw Samuele and Michael standing there across the patio with Stella and Angelo. Stella was standing there wearing a full apron waving a towel with her hand again. Oh my god, I have seen this before. *She must sleep in that thing,* I thought as I was laughing to myself running toward them with Jackie's lace panties bunched up in my hand. "We've been waiting for you, where have you been?" Michael said as Stella was handing Samuele Angelo's leash. "Here, Michael, take these and let Angelo smell them", I said as I handed him the lace panties.

"You are sick," Michael said as Samuele stood there laughing while Stella looked at me in shock. No, I'm serious, I got these out of Jackie's luggage and sprayed them down with her perfume, and Angelo needs to pick up a scent. Michael hesitantly took them from me with the tips of his thumb and index finger and gently wafted them in front of Angelo's nose. "There, are you happy now?" he said laughing. "Actually I was happy when I was asleep, thank you very much, so now what do we do?"

I said to the group.

"Well," Michael said. "Stella gave us a flashlight and told us to head down to the vineyard and olive orchard, it's the only place she could have gone as everything else is fenced off and gated. Samuele stood there with Angelo's leash, Michael had the flashlight, and I had the panties in case Angelo needed a refresher. We were ready to go. "Does Angelo need to be on the leash?" I asked Samuele.

"No, he needs to be able to search." *Okay*, I thought, *that's probably a good thing then because if I have my way, the leash is going on Jackie once we find her.*

Angelo was excited, and as soon as Stella gave him his command, he was off, running toward the olive grove, and within minutes he found Jackie. We heard him barking and ran toward the sound in the pitch-black darkness, tripping over dirt clods while trying to be careful not to run into a tree. When we got to Angelo, he was standing next to Jackie. She was passed out sound asleep against the base of an olive tree with one of her "hair enhancers" looking like a birds nest caught in a very low branch swinging in the breeze, just above her head. She had obviously had too much to drink and thought she needed to turn left, but for once turning left was not a good thing since the villa was on her right.

We each got around her and picked her up on the count of three then carried her back up to the villa, put her in bed, tucked her in, and vowed to never say a word thinking she would probably never know what happened anyway. Samuele then said, "But when she wakes up she will find herself in bed fully clothed, so should we—"

"No!" Michael and I said in unison. We're done; it's time for all of us to get some sleep, *buonanotte!*

CHAPTER 7

Ahoy at the Savoy

There are those mornings where you first wake up and want to stay in bed thinking about the night before while anticipating the day ahead, and this happened to be one of those mornings. I didn't stay in bed as long as I would have wanted because I could hear the clanking of glasses down stairs and the smell of fresh morning coffee. Always being one who never wants to miss out on conversation or adventure, I hurriedly jumped out of bed and went down to the kitchen to see who was up and what was going on.

Jackie had coffee going, and Michael was already up making fresh-squeezed orange juice. "How was everyone's night?" I asked them both.

"Mine was great," Jackie said. "I was so tired I don't even remember falling asleep. In fact, it was one of the best sleeps I have had in a long time, although I did wake up a little sore, but I'm sure it's because of the new mattress." Michael and I looked at each other; she didn't say a word about waking up in her bed fully clothed this morning, and we didn't say a word to her that she went tumbling down a hill into an olive grove.

Within the next hour there were people scheduled to arrive at the villa to start excavations for the pool and also to install the special fountain I had made for Marie. The three of us decided since the working part of our trip was really over and since Arnoldo the architect was going to be managing the outdoor work, it would probably be a good time for us to leave so that we could relax and get away from the noise of construction. As all I had to do was meet with Arnoldo, give him my vision of the courtyard and the placement of the fountain, and finish up the last few things that needed to be done inside. Once all of that was completed, we got our showers and packed our suitcases for the next leg of our Italian adventure.

We decided we wanted to stay two more nights so we could really experience all that Florence had to offer—the food, museums, nightlife, and shopping—so that's what we did. We drove into downtown Florence and checked into the Rocco Forte Hotel Savoy located in the famous Piazza della Repubblica. And although we were only about twenty minutes driving distance from the villa, this was going to give us a whole different perspective, especially since the hotel was

within walking distance of the Duomo, Uffizi Gallery, and the Ponte Vecchio. Arriving at the hotel by late mor-

ning, we still had much of a full day to plan. Jackie and Michael thought it would be a good idea to start off by going to a spa to experience total relaxation. I agreed and suggested going to the Montecatini Spa, especially since Jackie said her body was sore and Michael was walking like his was.

The hotel concierge told us it would be a wonderful time, he also suggested the experience, and said it's one thing not to be missed. I had heard about Montecatini in those "if you ever get the chance" stories from well-traveled people back home, and my mom even used to go to Nordstrom to buy Montecatini Miracle Mud in small glass jars that was supposed to make your skin look brand new in ten minutes for only thirty-five dollars. For all of these convincing reasons we agreed it had to be a good idea, so we drove to the famed Spa at the Terme de Montecatini, which was only about forty five minutes away.

When you arrive at the town of Montecatini, there are little signs that lead you to the spa. But the spa is not quite how we think of spas today. This spa is a small village of large ornate buildings that look like they are from the time of Cesar. And needless to say even with the signs we didn't know where to go, what to do, or even where to start once we got to the town. Considering we were now getting overly hungry we decided to just park the car and start walking around. We found one baroque styled building with dining tables inside and out filled with people eating lunch, so we stopped there to sit down and eat and tried to get everything figured out.

We ordered our food at the counter and at the same time asked the girl helping us if she could tell us where the actual spa was or how it all worked. She told us we were on track and doing the right thing. She went on to say we needed to first have lunch then walk out into the Grand Courtyard and over to Terme Tettuccio, where the wall of drinking fountains is located. Each fountain comes on at a specific time and runs for about two hours. The waters from each of the fountains contain different minerals which have supposedly been confirmed to be a curative for a plethora of different ailments.

"It's free," she said "You just put your glass up to the running water and drink. The drinking fountain coming on in the next thirty mi-

MONTECATINI WALL OF FOUNTAINS

nutes would be Leopoldina Waters. This water is indicated for the treatment of chronic constipation with normal bowel function generally restored whenever treatment cycles are spaced at four to six-month intervals. "But don't worry," she said with a straight face. "If you only drink one glass it will give you a very gentile release in about four hours, in fact you may not even notice." She continued saying that because of the rise in cultural demand for spas and spa treatments, all the original buildings are closed for remodeling and updating and would be open again next year. So in the meantime we could go to the more modern spa, Montecatini Aldo, which was a short drive just up the street about three miles.

It all sounded adventurous to us, and since we were out to have an adventure, we partook in the program. We relaxed in the restaurant, casually ate our lunch, and then walked over to have our glass of Leopoldina water. It was an exotic feeling getting healing waters from a several-thou-sand-year-old thermal source that had been brought to tepid temperature for drinking. We each filled our glass, which held about six ounces, then went over to a small table to sit down and enjoy the water. What we all quickly learned was that it had an extremely strong earthy and salty taste to it, not the type of water you wanted to sit down and take your time drinking. Jackie couldn't deal with it, so she gulped hers down. Michael and I tried to sip ours slow; in fact as it ended up, we didn't even drink half a glass each. "Well let's get to the spa," Michael said as if the water had just given him a lightning bolt of energy. So off we went to Montecatini Aldo, energized by our spa lunch and the healing Leopoldina water of Terme Tettuccio.

Upon our arrival and check-in to the spa, they advised each of us that bathing suits were required to check in, and if we didn't have one we could purchase them in the gift store located on the other side of the entry turnstiles—yes, like the kind they have at the zoo. They also advised us of the need to choose our spa package and pay for it before entering. Part of this was starting to feel strangely familiar, and the other part was just making me feel strange. But I didn't say anything, I didn't want to get Michael and Jackie unnecessarily stirred up as the potential for that was already there anyway.

So we said okay and we picked out our Spa packages. Michael chose the European Relaxation, herbal infused oil and hot rock massage; Jackie chose the full body sculpting mask wrap with warmed volcanic mud; and I chose the warmed olive oil hot rock massage. All of the treatments came with the use of the outdoor Terme pool, and each locker came with a one-size fits most terry robe to be worn to your treatment. We paid for our spa packages, and in exchange they handed each of us a plastic bag holding a green rubber bathing cap along with a token to activate the turnstile. We entered and went directly to the gift store to buy our bathing suits. Michael and I bought logoed swim trunks while Jackie bought a one-piece racer, maybe just to signify she was going nowhere fast. We agreed to get changed and then meet up at the treatment check-in counter, which was on the second floor.

Michael and I then entered into what was like a gymnasium locker room; the only difference is those have soap and this had nothing. I got changed and ready faster than Michael, so I went ahead and went upstairs to meet Jackie. When the elevator doors opened on the second floor, there Jackie was looking completely lost. "Oh good you're here," she said nervously, "this place is really strange!"

"Why, what's up?" I said as if I wasn't already having that feeling myself.

"Well look, it isn't modernized at all. Look down these long hallways; they are old peeling cement white walls with institutional-like doors on the rooms." I then told her I had a weird feeling when we checked in, but I didn't want to say anything.

"Oh my god," she said, "what are we doing here?"

"I honestly don't know, but don't worry," I said, "it will be okay, let's just go find the place to check in so they know we're here and we can wait for Michael." We then turned left and started walking down the hall, not knowing we were walking in a huge loop. In the meantime Michael got out of the elevator and thought he heard our voices so he turned right. He walked down the hallway passing door after door looking for us, but as he got closer to the voices he wasn't sure it was us. As soon as he turned into the room where he thought we were, he knew he had made a mistake. Sitting there on a table was a stark naked woman staring at him, looking like a baboon waiting for either an examination or a banana, with really sad boobs resembling ice cream cones that had been thrown against a wall. "What in the...?" We heard him yell from around the corner as we stood in the check in room.

"Michael, is that you?" Jackie said laughing while she looked out around the reception entrance to find Michael walking toward her barely wrapped in a terry robe two sizes too small. I just sat there thinking we really are at the zoo!

Once we had checked in for our treatments, the lady told us to go ahead and have a seat and they would be right with us. So Jackie and I sat down but of course Michael wouldn't, he couldn't. His robe was belted around him but holding on for dear life, barely closing in the front, and with any sudden shift or movement he would have been looking more like a cuckoo clock—yes, I said clock. Thank goodness he was the first one called in for his treatment. When she called his name, she handed him a small clear plastic bag with something in it. She told him it contained his undergarment to wear during his massage. He took it, looked in it, glanced back at us like a deer in the headlights on his way out and said, "They want me to wear this," as he held it up with two fingers. "Fine, I hope they're ready!" Jackie burst out laughing. "Oh no that's me," I said to Jackie when they called my name next. "Good luck," she said as the lady handed me my clear plastic bag and my undergarment. While I walked out the door with the attendant, I asked her if the undergarments came in sizes because no one asked me my size. She just said, "No, one-size fits most." I knew exactly what that meant.

When we arrived at my massage treatment room she told me to go ahead and get dressed, get on the table, and she would be right back. Dressed I thought, was I not understanding her? She then walked out leaving me there in a quiet and dimly lit room with amber votive candles glowing on the counter top and the smell of fresh herbs filling the air. I took off my robe, opened the bag, and pulled out my undergarment. I had never seen anything like it before in my life. It looked like a paper sling shot with rubber bands attached to each side. The paper was actually as thin as a piece of tissue and a little smaller than a coffee coaster, but in the shape of a triangle, sort of like an origami finger trap. Getting anxious thinking she was going to be doing the courtesy knock on the door at any time, I hurriedly tried to get my legs through each rubber band and right as I pulled up the piece of paper to get it in place, I looked down only to see what looked like Mickey Mouse with big ears falling out of a surgical mask. *Oh my god*, I thought, *it's upside down* as she barged in without the courtesy knock sounding like a mad dominatrix with broken English telling me to get face down on the table. Was she a complete idiot or just into it, I didn't know, but by then I was actually too nervous to care. I could barely communicate with her. So I got on the table face down, closed my eyes, and hoped for the best. She started pouring warm oil all over my exposed backside. Well, not completely exposed. She had two rubber bands to look at along with everything else.

Nervously lying there with all my muscles tense and on guard thinking I was only one stroke away from potentially being violated, how was I supposed to relax?

Then the hot stones arrived. We were in stage two, and I started to feel a little more at ease. As I laid there I started to think about Michael and Jackie, hoping they were okay having no idea of the drama that was really going on in their rooms. My massage finished, I got up, put on my robe, and went back to the locker room to put on my bathing suit since we were all supposed to meet at the pool.

When I arrived at the pool, I couldn't find them anywhere. They weren't lying by any of the poolside tables, and there had to be at least a hundred people in the pool, all wearing green bathing caps. *What now?* I thought as I became more and more frustrated. So I decided to just find a table and sit down. About fifteen minutes later here they come. "Where have you been? I've been looking for both of you everywhere, what happened?" I said as I saw Jackie walking toward me in a green rubber bathing cap and her racer looking madder than a transvestite who'd lost her wig at a Tina Turner look-alike convention.

"We'll," Michael said, "where do you want to start? This place is a joke; I am so mad I want our money back." Asking him again to tell me what happened; knowing Jackie was too mad to even speak right then, Michael went ahead and told the story. "First of all," he said, "I went in the massage room and tried to put that friggin' eye patch of a garment on, and as I was standing there on one leg while trying to put the other leg through the rubber band loop, the rubber band got caught on my big toe. I tried to get my big toe out and lost balance, fell backwards into the table, bruised the whole left side of my back, and ripped the paper right out of the band."

"So what did you do?" I said.

"I was so mad and didn't know what to do, so I got up on the table face down and waited for the therapist to arrive, I didn't care and thought she could just get an eyeful when I turn over!"

Laughing so hard I said, "So no one said anything about the elephant in the room?"

"She didn't say a word," he said. "I think the whole thing is planned, and it even gets worse! Jackie went to her treatment room and the table was covered in Saran plastic shrink wrap. The lady had her get on the table, completely covered her whole body from her neck to her toes with some kind of volcanic mud. Then she wrapped her whole body in the plastic wrap, put a blow dryer on it to shrink it tight, set a timer for twenty minutes and told her to relax. About five minutes later the Leopoldina water started to work on her, she felt like a Pompeii mummy and was ready to explode like Mount Vesuvius into a diarrhea attack, and no one was around. She somehow was able to get off the table, get her foot through the crack in the door and hobble herself out. Right then, thank God, I came walking out of my treatment and saw her standing in the hallway yelling for me, looking like a plastic wrapped human Tootsie Roll. She was yelling for me to hurry. I ran down the hall, unwrapped her, and got her to the bathroom. There was mud everywhere! It was a mess."

"Are you sure it was mud?" I said, laughing even harder as I envisioned Michael being only one pair of rubber pants away from having diapered a 150-pound naughty baby. I could hardly breathe. We all knew it was time to leave!

When we finally arrived back at the Savoy in the late afternoon, we decided to just spend the rest of the evening at our hotel since the local hot spot bar and restaurant L'Incontro was located right there inside on the first floor. It was presided over by Michelin star Chef Fluvio Pierangelini; making for what we thought would be a good evening, something we really needed, especially when we considered what our day had been like. But as it turned out we could not get into the restaurant for dinner as they were fully committed, but we could get in for early evening cocktails, so that's what we did. We went to the room, got changed into casual dinner attire, and went to L'Incontro. We had a really nice table right next to the bar, a perfect spot for people watching. As we sat there talking, I noticed a middle-aged man at the bar who had tried to inconspicuously swivel his chair and his ear around toward our table while he was doing something on his phone. We were talking about my niece's upcoming wedding, the dress designer, how many people would be at the wedding, where it was being held, just casual normal conversation. And right then this guy turned around and said, "I don't mean to interrupt"—yes he did, it wasn't an accident I thought—"but did you say you know Claire Von Atlenberg, the dress designer?"

"Yes, why?" I said.

"We'll I'm Manuel, nice to meet you all, and I'm very good friends with her." How could this even be, I thought?

We are halfway around the world, sitting in a bar talking and the guy across from us is friends with the person were talking about? He then began to try and become overly engaged with us, especially focusing in on Jackie, telling us he was also in the fashion business and that he owned the top fur and leather shop in the city, which just happened to be about a block down the street. "Really?" Jackie said. And that's all it took. Before we knew it, yes you guessed it. We ended up following him out of the restaurant like three of the seven dwarfs on our way to a shopping spree. He had a nice store with beautiful one-of-a-kind merchandise. When we entered the store there was a nice-looking older gentleman in a green striped shirt tending the store, who Manuel introduced us to before the man quietly left.

A lady assistant then came out from the back to assist Manuel as he carefully started draping furs onto Jackie with his over trained masculine touch. He knew his game very well, and I could tell he was picking up the fragrance of a newly divorced woman who was craving attention. But I couldn't say anything. Jackie was enjoying herself too much, and she was in her moment. After about thirty minutes of exaggerated personalized attention, she walked out with two furs, a crocodile leather belt, and a python purse that totaled close to twelve thousand dollars. He told her what the total was after he gave her a five thousand dollar discount. She was ecstatic, and Michael and I knew we had just watched something better than a Las Vegas Magic Show with a special assistant and all. Manuel said he would have all of Jackie's purchases sent over to the hotel so that she didn't have to be bothered with it. How big of him, I thought.

We left the store and walked back into the central plaza to get some dinner. Trying to keep things easy, we opted for an outdoor pizza restaurant. Although it looked touristy and the pizza looked high volume, what it lacked in taste we knew would be made up for in people watching. So we sat down, ordered, and tried to relax. It didn't take but about five minutes, and Michael said in a hushed surprised voice, "There's the guy in the green striped shirt walking around eyeing tables." We acknowledged what Michael was saying, but the tone of his voice was saying more. "What's going on, Michael?" Jackie said knowing Michael had spotted some-thing more going on behind her.

"Well, the guy is doing the same thing Manuel did to us. He just sat down at a table next to some well-dressed people who were almost finished eating then started working his phone, and now he is talking with them."

"You have the perfect view, keep watching," I said, "If Jackie and I turn our heads, it will look too obvious." Our pizzas and drinks showed up, we ate and laughed while Michael kept his eye on the target. "There they go," Michael said excitedly, "the people got up and walked off with the man." Once we finished our dinner we had to prove our suspicions, so we decided to go spy on the store. We approached the store from a different direction so that by chance we wouldn't run into them again. As we got closer we crossed onto the other side of the street and were able to get the perfect view. The man was standing next to his wife, who was standing in a three-way mirror while Manuel was on the other side draping leather jackets and furs over her shoulders while gently sliding his hands down her arms. Jackie let out a silent gasp; she couldn't believe her special moment with him looked as if he gave it to every woman in town.

"There you go, Jackie, we cracked the scam," Michael said, "but don't worry, you got some really nice things."

"Only if they show up to the hotel," I said. "No, I'm just kidding, don't worry they'll be there."

As we were walking back to the hotel, we noticed a sign that said, "Thursday Night Late Night Art Walk." It was the one night of the month when the art galleries and museums stay open late. We still had about three hours until closing so we decided to go since it would be our only chance to see Michelangelo's

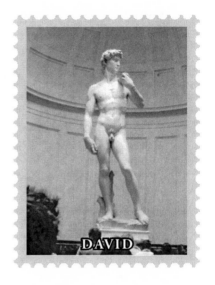

DAVID

David and his other works of art before we left Florence. We only had to walk a few blocks, and we were at the Galleria dell'Accademia, which is where the David lives. The line was only a few people deep, which rarely ever happens, so we got right in with little wait. There is a small collection of Michelangelo's work when you walk in leading to a short hallway that includes his four unfinished Prisoners and a statue of Saint Matthew. At the end of the hall is a large rotunda where you see the David. It is imposing and somewhat overwhelming, a spectacular work of art. The atmosphere was museum quiet and sort of contemplative until we got closer to the David, and Jackie blurts out, "Oh my god, he's so big!" I looked over at her and couldn't believe what she said. I could tell by the angle of her neck she wasn't looking at his feet.

"It's not real," I told her as she looked at me and said, "They never are!" Right then the lady behind us burst out laughing. Michael leaned over and whispered to me, "I think we've entered a woman's fantasy zone. Look around, we're the only two guys in here."

"We'll there's actually three if you count David."

MONA LISA CHALK ART

"Yes, but we can't compete with him, so let's move on to the next room." We both laughed and walked on. It only took us about forty-five minutes, and we were finished. Upon exit-ing the building we saw a group of art students doing chalk drawings right out in the middle of the town square on the street. The drawings were magnificent and impressive, especially the one I almost stepped on without realizing, it was the *Mona Lisa*. The evening suddenly became magical as we stood there under the evening shadow of the clock tower in town square watching the young art students draw. Hurriedly doing their chalk drawings of famous works of art as if they were heavenly angels who had just blown in for the evening to draw, only to disappear after adding a bit of visual enchantment for those lucky enough to see. As we continued our stroll under the warm evening sky, Jackie looked at us and said, "You know, I need to meet a man like you guys."

"Oh you will," Michael said, knowing he was safe since he had officially taken a sabbatical from dating.

CHAPTER 8

We're On Our Way to Pompeii

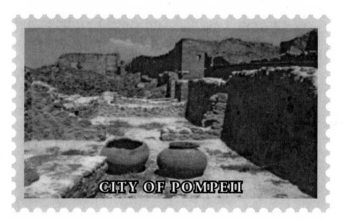

CITY OF POMPEII

The next morning we got up early and all met for breakfast downstairs in the hotel. We had another full day planned since the next leg of our trip would take us south to Pompeii and the Amalfi Coast. While at breakfast I told Michael and Jackie I had a surprise. I told each of them they were going to be treated to a private boat ride and an overnight stay at the best hotel in Capri, the Grand Quisisana, as a thank-you for all of the hard work they put into helping me at the villa. It was a splurge, and I knew it, but that's what creates lasting memories.

"Well what are we waiting for?" Michael said. "Let's go!" So the concierge arranged for a car to take us to the train station. When the car arrived, the driver got out and gave us the "I don't think so, this luggage is not going to fit" look, which was a look I had now started getting used to seeing. We told him not to worry; we knew how to make it work. I looked at Michael, and he looked at me while we did everything but slam our bodies against the luggage just to get it all into the car and get the doors shut.

When we arrived at the train station and opened the doors, most of Jackie's luggage went tumbling out onto the street. Michael quickly picked it up and slung it onto the sidewalk. Jackie's luggage had somehow now become mine and Michael's problem. Since Jackie was used to paying people to handle her luggage, she never worried about how much she brought. And no matter what we said, she still didn't seem to understand we weren't traveling that way, and there was no one to pay. Michael and I were the help.

Standing there with the luggage you could see what looked to be a normal flow of people change within minutes to a sea of people. "We better figure out quickly how we're going to move this luggage, the train is leaving in less than twenty minutes," Michael said.

"I know, how about we hook the two big roller bags together, and I can pull them. I'll let my bucket bag ride on top," Jackie said as if she had just come up with the latest invention for overluggaged travel.

"Okay, sounds good," I said not even wanting to try and figure it all out. So with Michael leading the way I followed behind Jackie, making sure nothing fell over or off. Walking through crowds of people like a moving company in a wedding procession, we were successfully able to navigate ourselves to the train deck. But now we didn't know which end of the train was first class, and no attendants were around to ask. When we finally found an attendant to ask, he told us first class was at the opposite end of the train from where we were. With now only minutes left before the train departed, we ran as fast as we could, dodging people, pets, poles, and trash cans. Pulling and pushing the luggage as it would serpentine back and forth, repeatedly falling over, hitting people several times before we made it to the opposite end of the train.

Of course we were tired, sweating, and frustrated after having run the distance of over thirty train cars. But our frustration even escalated more after we got the last piece of luggage onto the train. We stepped up, handed the conductor our tickets as we watched his lips dance to the words, "I'm sorry, but you're at the wrong end of the train, first class cars are at the opposite end." I believe it was right about that time when Michael added over five new words to the English language.

The train took off while we continued trying to find our seats walking up the aisle. As you can imagine once we found the correct cabin and our seats, we fell into them exhausted, we had begun our three-hour tour, and you all know how that famous one on television ended up for Gilligan. I should have known better than to sit in a seat where I was going backwards because about ten minutes after sitting down, I started to get motion sick. Looking out the window with the scenery going one way and me going another started to make my stomach feel like a high-speed blender on the frappe mode. I told Michael and Jackie I had to get up and get something to drink to settle my stomach. They both wanted something too, so Michael and I went together to find the concession bar and see what we could get. Luckily it was only two cars away. We ordered three coffees, three croissants, and some ice waters while I got my wallet out to pay. Michael said no, that he wanted to pay and to put my wallet away, so I did. We each tried to juggle three hot drinks, three cold drinks, and croissants back to our seats without spilling or dropping them as the train rocked back and forth, requiring us to have the balance of tight rope walkers. When we got back to our seats and distributed the drinks, Michael reached for his wallet, and it wasn't there. "Hey, Randy," he said, "did you pick up my wallet for me?"

"No, why, don't you have it?" I could see the look of panic on his face. "No, I don't have it, and I must have left it back on the bar counter when I was trying to pick up the drinks and croissants. We ran back to the bar and asked the attendant if he had the wallet or if he saw it, and guess what he said—No! We had just experienced our first encounter with European gypsy thieves. We stood there in shock, trying to replay what had happened only minutes earlier. I remembered seeing him pay, but I never saw his wallet after that. It had disappeared before our eyes just that quick. All of his credit cards and seven hundred and fifty dollars in cash were gone, someone on that train had it, and we knew it. We walked through every car looking at people, trying to possibly catch someone in the act of showing it to another person, counting the money or something. But every person just sat there looking straight ahead as if nobody knew anything. It is a helpless feeling when your time is running against the clock knowing the first stop is coming up shortly, and the thieves have the chance to walk off the train with your stuff. There was nothing we could do. We went back to our seats, and Michael immediately got on his phone and started calling his credit card companies, canceling all of his cards and arranging for a new credit card to be sent to our hotel. He was really upset, but we were determined not to let this ruin our trip.

Jackie was so mad, she opened her purse and handed Michael five hundred dollars with one hand while puffing her hair up with the other saying, "Don't worry, Michael, it's just cash. So take this, and when we get to Naples I am going to buy you a brand new leather wallet to put it in. I had read somewhere they are known for fabulous leather in Naples. In fact I really want a new pair of shoes from there anyway."

"Well what about me, what do I get?" I jokingly said.

Michael quickly replied without missing a beat, "What do you get? You get to go with us!"

About an hour later we arrived in Naples. Our hotel in Positano had arranged for a car and driver to pick us up at the train station, and just as promised he was right there waiting when we arrived. An extremely nice guy named Christiano, who was born and raised in Amalfi, and doing this work was his family business. He was very excited as this was one of his first assignments, and his father had given him the big Mercedes to drive, just in case there was a lot of luggage. It was obvious his father must have had previous experience with Americans and how they can tend to travel. Upon getting into the car he handed each of us chilled water bottles and asked where we would like to go first. We unanimously voted and asked him to take us first to the ruins of Pompeii and then to his favorite spot to eat. "Absolutely, let's go", he said.

Once we arrived outside the gates of Pompeii, the "City once frozen in time," I couldn't believe what I saw. Fruit stands with the most beautiful citrus fruit for sale that I had ever seen. Oranges the size of small grapefruits and lemons each the size of a football were being used by the stand keepers who were making and selling fresh-squeezed orange juice and lemonade.

CITRUS OF NAPOLI

The colors of the juice were so beautiful and vibrant, looking like it had been colored with food coloring, but it hadn't. So of course I had to buy each of us a glass of juice to drink and was so glad I did. The exceptionally cold fresh orange juice in the hot Pompeii heat was wonderful. You could feel the vitamins going into your system when you drank it, giving each of us the refreshed boost we needed to make the trek into the walled-off city. When you enter the gate they give you a typical guidebook to help you get the most of your inner-city excursion. It tells you all about the 79 AD eruption of Mt. Vesuvius, which covered the vacation town of Pompeii in a thick layer of ash, bringing the everyday life of its residents to an instant halt within a matter of seconds.

Carefully planned excavations have given way to the discovery of artifacts that have helped to accurately define life in Pompeii as it was before the disaster. Discoveries include bank receipts, mosaics, For Rent signs, homes, people, and so much more. But what I found most interesting was this intricately woven system of human needs and survival from almost two thousand years ago is not much different than ours today. As the three of us stood in one of the rooms looking at the preserved plaster casts of people instantly frozen in position when the ash poured over them from the sky made my mind wonder off into what it must have been like. It apparently had also prompted Jackie to wander off as well, not in her mind though but with her feet. Jackie had decided to put on some "instaflats" while in the exhibit. They were these disposable flat shoes in a zebra print that roll up into a small tiny can under vacuum pressure which she had remembered she had in her purse. She said she used them whenever her feet were swollen and she had to take off her shoes, so by the sounds of it she should had been an expert on getting them open. But this time when she unscrewed the can the shoes popped out like a can full of spring loaded snakes; one of them flew up in the air across the room and hit a woman next to me in the head. The lady screamed, I jumped, Jackie lost

her balance and fell, sliding down the steeped inclined stone pathway out of the exhibit that had been polished off like slick ice from years of use. Luckily Michael turned around just as Jackie went sliding down on

PEOPLE OF POMPEII

her back, only to stop herself by grabbing onto a railing post. Laying there on her back with one leg under her and the other in the air, she looked like a clothed version of the plaster cast volcano victims I had just been marveling at.

Everyone was worried she was okay, which she was, and no one but us seemed to speak English, so no real explaining could be done, except to us of course. "What happened?" Michael asked Jackie while he was picking her up.

"I'll tell you later, let's just get out of here, I've seen enough." Walking out barefoot she told us what happened, holding her heels in one hand and her program guide in the other. I couldn't help myself not to laugh.

"Where is the other shoe?" I asked.

"I don't know," she said, "The can must have been under a lot of pressure, I've never had this happen, the shoe went flying across the room and disappeared."

"Ya, into the side of that lady's head," I said while Michael laughed and said, "Well I think we need to disappear and get out of here too, let's go eat."

Thank goodness Christiano was waiting for us in the air-conditioned car just to the left of the exit. As soon as we got in the car he wanted to know if we were hungry. "Yes!" we all said at the same time. "And we want to treat you to lunch, so please take us to your favorite spot." He was not comfortable with us wanting to take him to lunch although he greatly appreciated the gesture as he began telling us where he was going to take us. Winding down a road that cut through a steep hill we could see the rooftops of beautiful rustic buildings in a storybook seaside village. "Is that where we are going?" I asked pointing out toward the ocean.

"Yes," he said, "I am taking you to a place that is truly Neapolitan, and the food is sensational. Typical Mediterranean cuisine according to the oldest local traditions, and during the summer time you can enjoy your meal on a beautiful terrace by the sea."

"What is the name of the restaurant?" Michael asked.

"It's called Mustafa," Christiano said with a big smile. "It's the perfect place for friends and family who want to spend a happy day."

Just as Christiano had said, they seated us on the terrace out over the water, and we were lucky enough to be the only customers there at the time. The menu was mouthwatering and rightfully so. We had entered the region of fresh Mediterranean seafood like no other place in the world. And so it goes, we started off with a bottle of wine and the Portobello mushrooms topped off with sautéed spinach, fresh mozzarella cheese, and sun-dried tomato pesto. That was followed by a sharable Capri salad of fresh mozzarella cheese,

151

tomato, fresh basil, and extra virgin olive oil. Michael was the appointed traveling Sommelier for our trip because he knew how to perfectly pair the wine with each of our meals. Jackie was the self-appointed menu drama queen that had to explain to every waiter across Italy about cross-contamination of shell fish with other foods in the kitchen—even if she was only ordering a pizza, which in this case she did. It was an entrée-size personal pizza that was beautifully designed and presented but not much different than a Capri salad on dough.

Michael ordered the Mediterranean grilled sea bass, and I ordered the linguini with white clam sauce. The setting could not have been more beautiful, the appetizers were exquisite, and the wine pairing was perfect. This for me is a big thing to say about wine as you know. And then the entrées arrived. The waiter approached the table from behind me so as all as I could see was Jackie's reaction as I was sitting across the table from her while Michael was sitting next to her on her right, so he couldn't see the look on her face. Jackie's mouth dropped open to which she quickly covered with her hand. *Oh no*, I thought, *what's happening?* It was the same sort of look that she gave when she approached the David in Florence, but that time she didn't cover her mouth. The waiter proceeded to put Jackie's pizza in front of her, my linguini in front of me, and last but not least Michael's fish in front of him. There were now four faces at the table, and three of them were staring at Jackie—me, Michael, and the fish while she looked like she was going to throw up.

"What's wrong?" Michael asked.

"I can't look at that fish looking at me," she said. I sort of understood but had come to terms with that long ago. Michael trying to be nice had the waiter take it back to the kitchen and remove the head. When the fish returned, it did look a little more Westernized, and Jackie seemed to be fine, well at least until Michael started eating it. "I can't eat anymore, I think I'm done," she said after only eating less than half a piece of her pizza. Why, we asked, is something wrong with your pizza?

"No," she said, "there isn't, it's just hard for me to eat when someone at the table has to pull bones out of the meat they are eating." *My god*, I thought, *can you just drink your wine, calm yourself down and get over all of your food issues already? How else is he supposed to eat his fish?*

Michael then looked at me like he was ready to ask them to bring the head back to the table so he could prop it up to stare at her while he finished his meal. As they say, two's company and three's a crowd. Lucky for me Michael's fish distracted her enough that she didn't notice I had shellfish on my pasta; otherwise I'm sure she would have been begging for one of us to stick it in again.

"Qualcuno ha Risparmiate spazio per il dessert di questa sera?" the waiter said when he returned to the table as we all gave him the same look that the fish had given us—a blank stare.

"Oh, forgive me," he said. "Did anyone save room for dessert?"

"Yes," Jackie quickly said as if someone was going to take it from her if she didn't immediately grab it off of the dessert tray. "I'll have the tiramisu." Michael and I both had the lemon sorbet. When we had finished I asked the waiter who made the lemon sorbet. He said for us to follow him and he would introduce us once we were finished, so we did. We walked into the main restaurant and saw a very sweet faced apron clad woman who just happened to be holding five large Sfusato lemons in her hand, I bet that's her, I said to everyone, and sure enough it was. We took a group photo and thanked them all for a wonderful meal as we departed for Positano.

While driving over the coastal mountain pass to the Amalfi coast, I started to smell something funny. Not knowing where it was coming from, I sort of just sat there and waited for it to pass, but it didn't. When I turned around to ask Michael and Jackie if they also smelled something funny, I saw that Jackie was asleep. So I looked at Michael and asked him.

"Yes," he said, "it's coming from over there," as he pointed to the other side of the car in Jackie's direction. I looked over and saw that Jackie had taken her shoes off. It was obvious here feet were not regulating to the heat of southern Italy. I felt bad for her as her ankles had turned to cankles; her calves looked like feet without taking an ankle break. "How much longer before we are there?" I asked Christiano.

"Only about fifteen minutes," he said as we crested the hill and were greeted by the Estoril blue colors of the Tyrrhenian Sea, sparkling like an ocean of diamonds in the sunlight, making you feel like something magical lay just beyond. This is it—I thought while looking out over hills of lemon and orange trees that gave way to a quaint Mediterranean village built against a seaside cliff—we have finally made it.

Christiano was not able to drive us all the way to the hotel but could only take us as far as the Piazza Dei Mulini. The hotel was down a narrow cobblestone pathway from there, which could only be accessed by foot or by a Cushman cart the hotel provided upon arrival. The path curiously wound itself down the hill about four blocks, passing storefronts and restaurants underneath a grapevine trellis dressed in bright pink and lavender bougainvillea.

The hotel only had two carts and we had to take both of course, one for the luggage and one for us. Driving down the winding cobblestone pathway to the hotel almost made you feel like you were on a ride through Pinocchio's village. It was quaint, charming and enchanted leading you to a small tiled sign that read Hotel Buca di Bacco. White Stucco and tile is the backdrop of this beachside retreat located on the Spiaggia Grande ("big beach"). As the story goes, the name of the hotel was born from the imagination of a group of artists who first discovered Positano as a holiday location. They created a romantic rendezvous spot for luxurious candlelit dinners out of a wine cellar. It was Gilbert Clavel, together with artist Lubbers and journalist Italo Tavolato, who invented the Buca di Bacco, where *Buca* means "hole" in Italian, referring to the cellar (thank goodness for that), and *Bacco* refers to the Greek mythological god of wine. This hideout for the rich and famous has inspired countless artist and famous writers, but was not really put on the map of common knowledge until well-recognized movie stars such as Elizabeth Taylor and Richard Burton made it their personal hot spot. And little did Michael and I know that Jackie was also hoping to make it hers.

When checking into the room they confirmed with me all of the requests we had made: separate beds, nonsmoking, ocean view, top floor, and breakfast included had been accommodated for with exception, they were not able to accommodate a connecting room. This was important as we wanted to be able to open the door between the rooms so that it would become like one large suite, making it possible for all of us to be together but yet have separate beds, dressing, and bathroom quarters. I explained to them when I made the reservations they had said they would be able to accommodate an adjoining room. "Oh yes," Stefano the front desk manager said, "we can accommodate an adjoining room, but that is different. An adjoining room would be a room next door to yours as none of our rooms have an access door in between."

"Okay," I said, "that's no problem, I am just glad I am here." Then he went on to tell me the second room was not going to be available for about an hour, so if we would like to have the entire luggage ensemble put into one room, they would do that for us, and then move it when the second room becomes available.

Stefano gave us the keys and up we went. The architecture of the building was 1930s. Stucco walls in and out, tile floors, curved lines on arches and doorways all done in a mixture of whites, yellows, blues, and greens. Visually enchanting in an Old World Italian sort of way, while very cooling to the senses by the colors they had used. There were no elevators, but only open-tiled stair cases presenting framed ocean views through subtropical planters that hung gracefully from the walls. The room was very well appointed in subdued shades of whites, oranges, blues, and greens with a large floor-to-ceiling shuttered door that opened out, creating a seamless view with the ocean, making it one with the room.

Jackie flopped on the chaise lounge, "This is it," she said, "I'm sleeping here, I'm not moving." *Right*, I thought, *with all your luggage there is no room in here, not to mention the bathroom would be continually hijacked by her and her bags of hair brushes, curling irons, lotions, solutions, spritzes, and sprays.* And the room only had one blow dryer, which looked like a small central vacuum system secured to the wall that blew out about as much air as I could get from fanning myself fast with a piece of paper. I could tell I was now getting stressed. Jackie got up and went into the bathroom. I looked at Michael and said in a hushed tone, "No really, Michael, I can't do three in this room, I just got out of a two-year relationship and broke off an engagement with a suffocating wacked-out woman, it's not going to work, and I really need my space. I mean look, even now I can't get into the bathroom, and the hijacking has already begun. I'm being forced to do the Macarena pee dance just so I don't wet my pants before she decides to saunter out with her freshly sprayed cockatoo hair. Can't you smell the hair spray? That's what she's in there doing."

"You think so?"

"Yes, I think so, one of two things is going to happen: She will either walk out looking exhausted, relieved and relaxed, and at that point you'll know the hairspray was an odor cover up, or she'll walk out looking stiff and happy, and then you'll know she was just in there teasing her hair."

"Well what if she walks out looking exhausted and stiff?" he asked.

"Well then that means all the above has happened, and you should call 911. I will take the other room, and you and she can have this room."

"I don't think so," he said back. "I'm going to take the other room, and you and her can stay in here."

Right then she walked out and asked, "What's going on, what you guys are talking about?"

"Oh," I said, "we were just thinking it would be a good idea if we go walk around town and explore a little bit, figure out where we want to have dinner, what do you think?"

"Yes," she said, "let's go." Which I was glad she did because what she did in the bathroom was still up in the air... literally.

Within several minutes of walking out the front door, Jackie spotted a small, sort of open-air cobbler shop that was dug back into the hillside like a cave with walls plastered over in white stucco. He was making shoes and sandals in every color and size while you wait with countless pairs hanging from the walls of which were all for sale. "Oh my god you guys, look at all the shoes," she said as she walked as deep into the store as she could. Had she stopped to think and forgotten to start again? What was going on? There was no more room to pack anything else and I definitely was not going to be carrying another bag. "These are so cute you guys, look at these!"

"Yes they are," I said as if I really even cared. "You should have one in every color."

"Really?" she said. "Yes really, they would all look great on you, don't you think, Michael?"

"Of course," he answered while looking the other way! Well we learned the hard way never to joke with a woman when she's shopping for shoes or when she asks your opinion when she's shopping for that matter, because the joke will be on you. And so it was.

Without a second thought she turned to the shop keeper and said, "Excuse me, could I have all of those on the top row in a size eight, oh and in every color?" And the four letter words flew out of Michael's mouth faster than a bread crumb lodged in his windpipe. "How's she going to carry those home?" he asked as if he was ready to make it clear that the past was not going to dictate the future. "Oh she's not, you are," I said as I laughed and walked out of the store.

We finally made our way up the hill and onto an even smaller side street. The most wonderful aroma of food was coming from somewhere on that street, and I was going to find it. So like the pied piper, Michael and Jackie followed me as I tracked where it was coming from. The menu on the sandwich sign at the entrance to the restaurant was like reading out of Lidia Bastianich cookbook. It had me at Frutti de mare marinara, and I wasn't going to let Jackie keep me hostage to her "Jackiefish" issues any longer. I didn't fight my way to the top of the food chain to be a vegetarian, pescatarian, or manipulated "catarian," and I could safely bet Michael was feeling the same way. The candlelit restaurant was probably a little too romantic for two guys and a girl. But what the heck, I was fine looking like the odd man out. So I decided to role play in my mind that Michael and Jackie were the couple and I could be their guest from out of town who had come to Positano to write a book and escape his busy life in the United States.

Michael ordered a bottle of wine for him and Jackie to share unbeknownst to my mind movie, underscoring my storyline of the evening while I went rogue. I ordered something I had never heard of, a Capri lemon drop made with locally sourced Limoncello.

"You're having a martini?" Michael said in shock. "I've hardly ever seen you drink a glass of wine!"

"Well tonight that may change," I said as I slowly sipped the most refreshing, smooth exotic drink I had ever had in my life. "Now this," I said, "is La dolce vita, cheers everyone!" Making our way back to the Buca di Bacco we decided to go a different direction that took us along the waterfront. A completely different atmosphere than the one you see during the day. Large gently lit private yachts were resting in the bay, and the coastline was magically glittering with strings of café lights dancing in the breeze above us like fireflies in the sky.

The soft sound of Italian music was floating through the air while muffled voices of people talking and laughing lulled me into a wonderfully relaxed state. Or could it have been the three Limoncello lemon drops I had just had a visit with. Oh well, either way it didn't matter as I knew my bed was waiting for me only minutes away.

When we arrived at the hotel we were greeted by Stefano,  who let us know the second room was ready and all the large pieces of luggage had been moved. *Ah those are Jackie's*, I thought, *how did he know to put hers in there?* "If you'd like to follow me, I will show you all to the room," he said in a very calming voice. By the look on Jackie's face I could tell she was excited the numbers had just increased: she now had three men going with her to her room. As he opened the door you couldn't help but be mesmerized by the size of the room that was in front of us. It was huge, taking over what looked like the majority of the third floor. From its location the overindulged suite had breathtaking panoramic views of the bay looking out toward Capri. This perfect Italian room was a retreat in its own right, boasting an impeccable design, spacious layout, and every amenity one could wish for.

Throughout the suite, handcrafted rugs and unique artwork existed alongside stunning artifacts and furnishings, all tied together by a yellow and light blue color scheme accented with luminous brushed gold, white, and deep red accessories. The two bedrooms featured upholstered silk headboards with contrasting walls and spacious walk-in closets paneled with lemon wood. Equally stunning were the adjoining bathrooms, outfitted with honey onyx and tile walls featuring oversized tubs and glass-enclosed steam showers. Furnished with custom-designed pieces, the large living and dining area were serviced by a gourmet kitchen and purposely placed on a center table was a bouquet of twenty-four white long stem roses, which I noticed had a small card nested inside. The room offered a true sense of luxury and space; they had given us what would arguably be the most impressive, soothing and stylish room in the city. "This room upgrade comes with complements of the hotel manager," Stefano said. "If there is anything else you need, please press the number 1 on your phone, and either me or your personal concierge will make sure all your needs are immediately tended to," He glanced quickly over at Jackie and continued, "We hope you enjoy your stay with us."

"Well, who gets this room," I said sort of jokingly, "I know you don't want it, Jackie, since you already made claim to the other room and said you weren't moving."

"But my luggage is already here so I will go ahead and stay in this room," she said as Michael began to say it would be no problem to carry her luggage back to the other room and give her what she really wanted. She looked at him with excited surprise.

"I'm talking about the room Jackie, so calm yourself down," he said while halfway nervously laughing.

"Good night, everyone, I'm going to bed, it's getting way too late," I said as my intuition was telling me the best thing to do was to leave Jackie in that room even though it would have been a much bigger room for Michael and I to share since it did have separate bedrooms and bathrooms. "Oh don't go to bed yet," Jackie said, "I think it would be fun to go out and walk on the beach, do you want to?"

"No", I said, "and you shouldn't be going out there by yourself either, we don't need you disappearing, and its way to late anyway. Let's just all get some good sleep, and we can regroup in the morning." It was becoming obvious to me one of two things was going on. She was either trying to manipulate the situation into one where she gets a roommate for the next three nights, or she wanted to be alone so she could call up the front desk manager to act on his departing words. I'm smart enough to know she wasn't planning on staying in the room alone that night just so she could sit on the bed and play with all her shoes as if she was Imelda Marcos.

As soon as I got into the room I went to bed and fell right asleep, but it seemed as though not much time had passed, and I was awoken by the light of the moon shining over the water through the opened shuttered doors. Lying in my bed awake I now knew I would have to get up and close the shutters to darken the room if I was going to be able to get back to sleep. As I lay there for a few minutes negotiating with myself whether I could fall back asleep without getting out of bed, I started thinking about that room, remembering there was a card in those roses that were on the table. Hmm I thought, I wonder who those were from, or was it just something they put in the room as a welcome gift like a fruit basket?

I finally got up out of bed and walked over to the shuttered doors, taking a quick look out over the beach, I stood there in shock as to what I saw. My intuition was right; Jackie was walking down the beach with a guy that looked very much like Stefano. "Michael, are you awake!" I quietly yelled over to his bed.

"I am now."

"Hurry get over here, Jackie is out on the beach walking with some guy."

"Are you sure," he said.

"Ah yes I'm sure…she isn't walking with a pelican." He got out of his bed and came over saying what we were both thinking—we've got a mess on our hands.

The next morning we made a pact we weren't going to say anything or ask questions that might indicate we were onto whatever she was up to. I called her room to make sure she was up and ready to meet for breakfast, and she was. I told her Michael had already left to get a table, and I was just getting ready to leave, so we planned to meet out on the breakfast terrace as soon as she could. It was a beautiful ter-race scattered with lemon and orange trees in large clay pots. The citrus blossoms were abundant, mixing their fragrance with the jasmine and stephanotis blooms that were growing on vines along the stucco walls. We put in our breakfast orders and then were invited to squeeze our orange juice from a machine filled with fresh-picked chilled oranges. It was an Italian-made machine designed to let you just press a button and through a cage you could see the orange roll down, get sliced then squeezed while the juice flowed freely into your chilled glass. I guess I still get excited over the little things in life.

The waiter first brought out our café lattes, which were top-ped with a thick layer of cream almost the

HOTEL BUCA DI BACCO TERRACE

consistency of custard; it was quite unbelievable and quickly became my addiction for the rest of our time in Italy. This was a breakfast you just didn't want to end, but had to because this day was going to be our full day at the beach, and we wanted to make sure we were there in time to secure our orange-padded beach lounger chairs. Walking down to the beach Jackie realized she had forgotten her beach sunglasses in the room, so I said I would run back up to get them for her while she and Michael took care of getting the beach chairs. She told me the glasses were either in her Vuitton bucket bag or they were lying on the table next to the roses. "Okay, no problem I will be right back," I said as I turned and walked away.

When I went into the room I could tell housekeeping had not yet cleaned the room, there were two used wine glasses on the counter, but no sunglasses. There was also a short see-through baby- doll-style night gown in the corner, and the bed sheets looked like they had been blown over by a tornado. Not wanting to see anything else I possibly shouldn't, I looked down and saw her bucket bag sitting on the table next to the roses I looked inside and couldn't see anything; it was full of more junk than a month-to-month storage unit. So I dumped it over onto the bed watching more fall out than a nuclear power plant. Oh yes, the sunglasses fell out, and so did the opened card that had been nested into the roses.

Jackie, please accept these as a token of
my admiration for you, enjoy your stay
in Positano.

—Tanto Amore, Samuele

Oh this is going to be really interesting I thought, and of
course, I couldn't wait to get back to tell Michael the mystery
of the room was slowly being revealed.

It was a fun day swimming in the ocean, laying out
and watching all the people parade along the sea shore in
there scantily clad Riviera wear, or as I call it, no-rear-end
wear, wearing lots of jewelry obviously never intending to
get wet. While I was lying on my chair I happened to notice
a sandwich sign (they're really into those in Italy) that read,
Boats for Rent. I asked Michael and Jackie if they wanted
to walk over and check it out. Of course Michael did, but
Jackie just wanted to lie there and keep working on her impossibly dark tan. I was ready to start calling her Magda of the
Mediterranean. If you ever saw the movie *Something about
Mary*, you know what I'm talking about.

So we walked over and spoke with the man in charge of the rentals and made a deal with him for his company to take us over to Capri the next morning. He was a nice guy and his name was Guido, but let me just tell you, when you have a name like Guido or any name with more than one vowel, it's your job to check your breath several times a day, especially before introducing yourself. You have no excuse. God knew what he was doing when he placed your nose above your mouth; it was for a reason, so use it. His breath smelled like old salami with a sardine chaser, not something I was excited about him sharing with us. Thank goodness I had mastered the art of circular breathing, just like Kenny G many years ago, so I resorted to doing that while we made the deal with him. When we were done, I was sure Michael had negotiated the best deal possible, and we were really excited.

Quickly we went back to tell Jackie hoping she would also be excited, but the first thing out of her mouth besides her tongue was "What about the room?" I told her we can have the hotel hold our room here over night for us as Michael reiterated to her again that we were going to an overnight in Capri and staying in the best hotel on the island in one big room, almost like an adult slumber party! He had obviously just said two of her favorite words, "big room" and "party," as she jumped up faster than Mamma Cass grabbing a ham sandwich and gave each of us a big hug.

Just as planned we awoke early the next morning with our overnight bags packed. Jackie of course had packed two bags, one for all her stuff and the other for the rest of her stuff. After having another wonderful breakfast out on the terrace we went back to our rooms to make sure we had everything we needed and to change out of our clothes into our bathing suits. On our way out we stopped by the front desk to let the front desk manager know we would be out overnight so if they needed to reach us for any reason to please use our cellular phones. He smiled and said in Italian, "Upon your arrival, open your hearts and you will see, engraved upon it the island of Capri. Have a magical time." I knew he was trying to be nice, but he sounded a little too much like a retired washed up Disneyland guest greeter.

Walking down the cobblestone steps winding graciously through the quaint shops on the way to the beach Jackie said that something was on her mind that she needed to tell us about, but would wait until we were at dinner. Why in the world did she need to tell us that, especially so early in the day? Did she think she was being thoughtful because she was giving us ten hours to think about what it could be? I always think people who do that are either stupid or just plain rude, like the people who tell you about the gift they almost bought you. So without knowing how to reply I simply said, "Oh I can't wait, dinner is going to be so much fun as that will then be the perfect time for me to tell you what the front desk manager said to me about you. Oh look, Guido is waving to us." Looking over next to him, I saw a large motorized water raft with a younger-looking guy loading on a water cooler and ice chest.

"That must be our captain," Michael said. The closer we got you could tell he wasn't as young as he had appeared from a distance. I think it was his head of hair that seemed peculiar as it came more into focus. Having an obvious eggplant colored tint job over his somewhat brown-colored hairline made it look like a small animal was sleeping on his head. But the real question was answered when we approached the boat. A small breeze picked up, lifting the "hair" off of his bald head like a Swiffer on a hardwood floor, I tried not to look as he quickly scrambled for his "Captains hat."

"Good morning, Guido," we all said. "Is this our boat?"

"Yes, it's your Zodiac raft," he replied. "And I would like you to meet Antonio; he will be your guide today." We talked with them both for about ten minutes more, setting up our return arrangements while giving him our carry-ons, and then we were off to Capri.

It was a beautiful ride along the Amalfi, watching the ocean splash and spray upon the coastline as we looked out onto old ruins and castles woven into a tapestry of alleyway mazes and narrow rock hewn staircases leading to houses and gardens found clinging to the rocks. There were hidden coves, inlets, and small villages punctuating this legendary stretch of coast between Punta Campanella and the Bay of Salerno. And just beyond in the distance you could see the *faraglioni:* Stella, Mezzo, and Scopolo jutting out of the water like Herculean monoliths, but it was the Island of Capri that sat out in the ocean as the crown jewel. Sparkling in the sun and shrouded in exotic history with secrets to tell of the rich and famous that had once made this rock their home and playground in days gone by. Without sounding like a bad game show host, I have to say this trip was now going to be our grand showcase prize for two days and one night.

CHAPTER 9

Just Us Three in Capri

"Welcome to Capri, My name is Alto," a man who looked like Fabio but small enough to fit on a charm bracelet, said to us as we disembarked our luxury yacht (rubber raft) at the main entry port of Marina Grande. "Will you need a taxi?" he asked as Antonio handed him our overnight bags to which he all but disappeared behind.

"Yes," we said, and as if out of nowhere a cerulean blue car with a

TAXIS OF CAPRI

matching striped awning roof appeared. It was our taxi and would be taking us to our hotel. Everything was completely *Fantasy Island*-esque and we even had our very own Italian version of Tattoo. I wanted to ask him to say "De plane, de plane" just for kicks but didn't want to be rude, remembering I once said something to a small dog and it bit me.

While putting everything into the backseat of the open-air car, we told Antonio we would call him the next day when we were ready to be picked up. Then all three of us got into the car sitting on the middle bench seat like we were ready to go on a theme park ride. Jackie pulled a scarf out of her bag and within a blink of an eye she had it wrapped around her head looking like Gina Lollobrigida doing an ad for Guess? large dark glasses and all. With her scarf and our hair blowing in the wind we were on our way up the lemon tree–lined hill to the Grand Hotel Quisisana. What we were not aware of was the taxi could only take us to what the locals refer to as the *chiazz* or *piazza*, to the rest of the world it's the *piazzetta* or Piazza Umberto 1, Capri's most famous square. But no matter what you call it, one thing everybody can agree on is this is the place to come in the evening to people watch. Our driver told us the square would be full by 9:00 p.m. with the worlds' most fashionable and beautiful people walking around while others casually sip their coffee and cocktails at one of the many wicker café tables sitting softly lit in the shadow of the world famous blue- and yellow-faced white stuccoed Clock Tower. A paparazzo's nighttime playground reminding you that stars are all around and not only in the evening sky. Once we reached the Piazzetta, a small passenger cart would take us the rest of the way, down a long and narrow cobblestone street. The street was lined on both sides with the most expensive boutiques in the world giving way to the warm yet somewhat imposing, elegantly decorated white-and-yellow courtyard that stood as a threshold to the entrance of the Grand Quisisana.

We were now deep into the world of the lifestyles of the

GRANDE QUISISANA HOTEL CAPRI

rich and famous, and I could feel it. I could also feel the reality of showing up in a rubber raft and schlepping in with nylon backpacks, trek shoes, and multipurpose bathing shorts. The only saving grace was I could hide behind my understated but equally affective tortoise shell Ray Bans while Michael wore his large black Ray Ban Wayfarer 57s, giving him the look of a movie star you just can't quite place. And Jackie, well, I don't even know by this time what was going on, but something had changed. Maybe it was the lighting in Capri, or did she change her glasses? She was now looking more like she could have been the love child of a brief affair between Gloria Swanson and Cary Grant or Cary Grant and Elton John, readers' choice. But in any event definitely more conservatively alluring than the sexy Gina she had just started out looking like merely thirty minutes before. As I looked closer I figured it out; it was the scarf and the glasses.

She had untied the turban letting her long locks of black hair flow over her shoulders in a carefree "I just walked off my yacht" look. The scarf was now gently draped and tied on her head in a bandana style securely covering the stems of her sunglasses, which had changed to a miniature black Ray Ban version of Michael's. I was beginning to think her Louis Vuitton bucket bag was carrying more tricks than the bag of Felix the Cat.

Upon walking into the hotel to check in you could easily look around and tell this was a destination that has attracted an exclusive crowd since its opening in 1860. It can now be said that over the years, historical figures such as Ernest Hemingway and Jean Paul Sartre and the three of us have passed through the marble lobby to enjoy the regal beauty of the hotels rooms, food, pool and manicured grounds. That and three seventy five will buy me a latte at Starbucks. Big deal, but okay, it was fun for the Cinderella moment that it lasted.

We checked into our sun-drenched room, which they say is a study in understated elegance, with mostly white walls, floors, and furnishings emphasizing the array of colors the ocean had to offer on this perfectly Capri day. Once we got settled and unpacked we decided first to take in some lunch poolside then float around the pool having drinks on our water loungers. They sat us at a beautiful table covered in white linen with a centerpiece of fresh jasmine and gardenias; they are very much into white. The food was perfectly prepared and impressively presented looking like the still shot from a high-end high gloss tabletop magazine. And the best part of all was we were alone, no kids, no chatter, or the smell of luncheon lady's overly sprayed perfume. It was just the three of us and the sound of the birds and the ocean breeze gently moving through the trees serenading our senses with an aria from nature. Well at least until the Glickmans showed up.

"Over here, kids, let's take this table, set all your stuff in the empty chair and we'll wait until Mom comes. Noah, Batia, what would you like to eat?" he said in a rushed "I can barely breathe" loud obnoxious camp-counselor voice.

"Oh great, the ark just showed up", I said to Michael and Jackie, to which Jackie replied as she looked straight on behind me, "Oh, you have no idea!" I didn't want to be too obvious and turn around, but my imagination was getting the best of me, and I had to see who the family was that reeked of *Bounce.* As luck would have it, I didn't have to turn around because within seconds a small floaty ball landed on Michael's pizza di Scarole with Cetara's anchovies (never mess with Michael's anchovies) after the word "catch!" was yelled by who I assumed was Noah.

"How many times have I told you not to play catch at the table with your sister?" the man said as if he really thought the question was going to make a difference. "Hi, I'm Morty

Glickman," the short round hairy man said as he approached Michael with his hand outstretched. "I'm really sorry about the ball, my son has been having anger management issues lately, and so my wife Chava and I decided we would go ahead and bring the kids on our dream vacation with us. We were hoping if we spend a little more time with them, as his behavioral therapist advised, then we had a good chance he may snap out of it."

I couldn't believe what I was hearing, I wanted to tell him he was the one that needed to snap out of it, that was until I saw his wife Chava in her bright patterned stretch smock barely covering her overly pilled white stretch leggings as she walked down the garden path toward the table yelling, "Hey, Morty, order me a large orange juice!" This immediately underscored for me the accuracy of the Bible when God told Noah they would be brought to the ark in two's. I could see history repeating itself right before my eyes.

"Oh hi everyone, I'm Chava, we just got here."

Oh really? I thought. "Where are you all from," I said trying to be nice.

"We're from Southern California, isn't this place just the bomb? I mean look at this, it's absolutely gorgeous. I don't know how we would have evah been able to afford this kind of trip, but we were so lucky we won it in a raffle at a travel agent convention, right, Morty? I'm not a travel agent, but we went to see what kind of savings we could get on travel if we became one, and you know I never sign up for things but this time I did, something just told me to fill out the piece of paper and put it in the jar, first time evah, I'm still in shock. Morty got the call, right, Morty?

"We just couldn't believe it. That was on Thursday and look before you know it here we are. I mean it's like blink, and here I am. Oh my gosh! Have you ever had something like that happen to you? Oh, wait what were your names again?"

Jackie looked at Michael and me and said, "Do you think I can blink and make them go away?"

Michael quickly replied, "I don't know, why don't you try."

"I'm Randy, this is Jackie and this is Michael," I said.

"Oh how nice, I'm Chava." I was so irritated by this point I looked at Michael and said, "I wish they would bring her some food and Chava some of it into her mouth already."

We tried to be nice while at the same time distancing ourselves as much as we could, not that they weren't nice, but it was apparent their issues had issues, and like a tar baby if we got too caught up with them, all of a sudden their issues would be ours, and we would be stuck.

"Oh excuse me, Michael," Morty said, "do you know if this is a buffet, you know sort of like all you can eat? We love to do those in Las Vegas, don't we, Chava?"

"Oh yes, it's such a value you know, it's like I just stand  there looking at all the food and realize for $24.99 it honestly could all be mine, but then I come to my senses and opt for only a couple of plates, oh my." They didn't even realize Michael never answered them because the waiter came up to take their order and to see how we were doing. We told him we were fine but wanted to know if it would be okay if we moved our drinks and the few plates of hors d'oeuvres over to the poolside tables. He told us that would be no problem; in fact, he even helped us set up at a beautiful little table with three poolside loungers.

Finally we were able to relax again, talking and laughing and really having a fun time together. Jackie decided she wanted to go ahead and take her drink into the pool with her, float around, relax, and enjoy the scenery and sunshine from a water lounger while Michael, for the time being, just wanted to swim. The attendant brought over three water loungers just in case, and then we all put on our sunblock, and Jackie got into the pool.

I would have to say this was really Jackie's movie star moment. Here she was in her black bikini with gold hoops, hair piled high on her head with her Ray Ban Wayfarers perfectly placed as she calmly floated with her wine glass alone in a pool that looked like glass. Michael went over to the refreshment station to get a pitcher of ice water for us, and I decided to just lie on the chair and relax. Just as I had closed my eyes, I heard Michael yell from across the pool, "Jackie, watch out!" Morty had decided it was his time in life to jump into the pool cannonball style. I can't really even describe the sound other than it sounded like a huge block of air got sucked into a vacuum and then imploded. I opened my eyes just as the water hit Jackie's perfectly stacked up pile of hair falling down covering her eyes while hitting her in the face like a fallen soufflé. She screamed and dropped her wine glass into the pool. I could tell that was it, Michael's zodiac sign is a Taurus and the bull had now emerged. Michael turned around, walked over to the attendant and told him he needed to take care of the situation immediately if not sooner, and if he didn't, then Michael would. If I had to pick I would say having Michael do it would probably not be the best choice; that would be more of a last resort, no pun intended.

Lying there I could hardly believe what had just happened. Michael got into the pool, helped Jackie retrieve the wine glass as she got off of her lounger to go under water and get her hair out of her face. Michael and Jackie got themselves resituated on the water loungers while the attendant called the hairy thunder ball over to the other side of the pool. I'm not sure what he said to him, but Chava finished it off, looking like she was telling Morty whatever the attendant may have forgotten to say. Her mouth was now going faster than she ate, and her hands weren't far behind. For some reason I don't think that was the first time nor was it going to be the last. I went ahead and joined Michael and Jackie in the pool laughing in disbelief. "What was that all about," I said to Michael.

"I don't know and I don't want to know, but they better take care of it!" Then all of a sudden Chava appeared poolside. She wanted to apologize for her careless husband, but the three of us could hardly pay attention to what she was saying. And quite honestly, I don't know how anyone could. She was standing there in her one piece bathing suit the size of Africa with a Spanx girdle peeking out under the leg bands, she should have just opted for a burqini! The latest swimwear favored by some Muslim women that covers everything. What was she thinking? It was right then and there I decided to write Spanx a letter telling them I had just come up with a new product line: Spanx for bathing suits. They would come in three sizes, small/medium would be called Spank It, medium/large would be called Spank Me Hard, and large/extra-large would be called Spank Me Harder. I think it's going to be a big winner.

You would think the day we had just come off of would have brought more than enough drama for a full week, but we still had more to come. There was still the confession at din-

ner from Jackie, at least that's what Michael and I were anticipating would be Jackie's tell-all drama that she intimated to
when she said she had something to talk to us about. We
knew she had some "splainen to do," as Marky Ricardo used
to tell Lucy, but we still could not let on that we knew or saw
anything.

So we set up dinner at Capri's Ristorante Faraglioni,
which is famous throughout the world for its excellent traditional cuisine, its unbeatable location, and last but not least,
its wine menu featuring over six hundred different bottles of
Italian and international wines. It is located down the final
stretch of Via Camerelle, which is a small quaint pedestrian
road. Outside seating at the restaurant consists of traditional
canopies on one side of the road. They are made of straw
and transform each table into an exclusive and intimate little
dining room, on the other side is a dining pergola wrapped
in over a one-hundred-year-old wisteria, setting the backdrop
for both privacy and romance. We chose the tables with the
straw canopies. This would be a sure bet to make for a relaxing evening while at the same time creating the perfect envi-
ronment for Jackie to spill, and I don't mean the wine.

Our meal could not have been better. From the first taste I was reminded again how sensuous food can be. The food preparations were seductively original in their presentations giving a new experience to familiar flavors making every bite almost a requiem to Capri, especially the lemon risotto, which deserves to be a whole conversation all on its own. After our meal and their several bottles of wine later, I thought ample time to hear what Jackie had to offer had been given, especially since as of yet she had said nothing. So with a beautiful dessert assortment at the table along with a bottle of ice cold limoncello, I decided it would be my job to bring up the conversation.

"Oh, Jackie, I just remembered, didn't you have something you needed to talk to Michael and me about? I'm so glad I just remembered and didn't forget because it sounded really important to you, what is it, did you get a call from your attorney?"

"Well actually yes, I did get a call from my attorney, and the divorce is final. Tom has in so many words been forced to agree with the terms. I have to tell you, Randy, if it wasn't for you I may not be walking away with more than him."

"Why is that?" I asked. "Well, the information you gave me in the beginning about Tom's indiscretions put him in a position where he wasn't sure what all I knew, and he didn't want to take his chances finding out, that could have cost him millions more. So he decided to play it safe and agree to give me more in the settlement," she said with a look on her face as if to say, "What an idiot he is."

"All good news," Michael said in an excited and exuberant voice. "This deserves a toast!" So there we were having a limoncello and red wine toast under the midnight blue and starry sky of Capri, still not knowing for sure what Samuele was up to, or Jackie for that matter. I decided not to push the conversation in that direction as I didn't want to come across as possibly knowing something or even being interested. "Let's walk up to the piazzetta, watch people and have a drink are you both in for that?" Michael said.

Jackie looked at Michael and said, "Are you kidding, I couldn't think of anything better right now than watching people in the piazzetta while having another glass of wine. It's my magical night in Capri!" As we left the restaurant walking back on Via Camerelle to the piazzetta, there was a small sidewalk flower shop filled with roses and flowers of every kind and color. It was an enchanted shop seeming to stop lovers in their tracks who were out for an evening stroll. "Did you guys know that every color of rose has a meaning to it?" I casually said as we walked by.

"Hmm," Jackie said while we continued walking. Several minutes later she asked what white roses meant. I explained that white roses are traditionally associated with new beginnings, but their quiet beauty also makes them a gesture of remembrance. A bouquet of white roses is a perfect way to say "I'm thinking of you."

When we got to the piazzetta it was just as our driver earlier in the day had told us, but what I had translated into big fashion, big hair, and big attitudes.

PIAZZETTA CAPRI

This is going to be great I thought as Michael found us the perfect table to take in the evening show of beautiful people and haute couture. "Haute couture" is a French word used throughout the world to describe the utmost high-quality yet exclusive fashion. It is fashion constructed by seamstresses using hand-executed techniques without the use of sewing machines from start to finish. It is well known that price is not relevant to the budget of people who wear haute couture as they generally have no price tag. I could tell by the look in Jackie's eyes what she was thinking. She was officially divorced, and it was now her time to indulge in more than another glass of wine; she wanted to add haute couture to the new life she had waiting ahead.

Knowing we were only five days from going to Paris, she asked us if we could help her find a few haute pieces possibly at Channel and other boutiques. Of course we both told her yes, while I added in that she could also have an exclusive French perfumery mix her own signature fragrance to round out the experience. She asked me what fragrance I liked best on a woman. Of course my first thought was soap but quickly jumped over that to white flowers. As white flowers always have the most elegant transforming fragrance. "In fact speaking of white flowers, Jackie, did you ever find out what was up with that big bouquet of white flowers in your room?" I asked. "Oh I wanted to tell you guys about that, yes I did, they were from Samuele. Wasn't that nice? It was so unexpected." It always bugs me when people tell me something obvious was so unexpected. She went on to tell us that when Samuele found out we were staying at the Buca di Bacco, he called ahead to his friend who happens to be the general manager and arranged for her to have the Grande suite. So with that, Michael ordered each of them another glass of wine and a lemon drop for me; he knew the story could only get better.

Contrary to popular belief, I might have been born at night, but it wasn't last night, and I don't have any brain function loss that I know of, so why was this not adding up for me? We never told Samuele where we were staying, although we did mention to him we were going to Amalfi, but that's a big area. Jackie continued to talk, putting out a lot of words but still not saying much. "Wow, what a surprise," I seamlessly said interjecting into the conversation as I kept trying to connect the dots. When she finally came up for air to take another drink, now on her fourth glass of wine from their third bottle of the evening, Michael knew it was his time to ask, "Well what about Stefano, how does he fit in?" Oh my gosh, I thought, I couldn't believe Michael took the leap, and without missing a beat Jackie said, "He's great!" What was that supposed to mean? Now, she's not making any sense. Had she drank too much, which meant we weren't going to get the rest of the story, or was she just messing with us?

"No, Jackie, I think what Michael is asking is, does Stefano know Samuele, or how did this all happen? I mean it's hard to figure out how or why Samuele would pay so much money for this room upgrade even though Stefano said it came with compliments from the hotel manager, it just doesn't make any sense." Jackie looked at me slightly slurring her words and said, "Randy, you just don't understand." Oh great, I thought, we now have *Baby Jane Hudson* on our hands, and this story is going to have to wrap up. I knew it was time to go.

As we left the piazzetta, Michael casually helped her up knowing it could be a challenge for her in the shoes she had chosen for the evening. A five-inch black leather pump with leather tassels on the back slapping her heel with every step she took. Was she living out a fantasy in those shoes? Holding onto Michael's arm I heard her say again, "Michael, he just doesn't understand." Walking a few steps behind I looked at her in those dominatrix shoes and hummed the theme song from Whatever Happened to Baby Jane? "I'm sending a letter to Daddy…" while still trying to figure out how to just buck up and ask her, "Who's your daddy?"

The next morning we woke up early since it was our last day in Capri, and we wanted to make it as full a day as possible. It was now 8:00 a.m., and we were on our way down to have breakfast poolside while I silently prayed the Glickmans would still be in bed snoring on their CPAP machines or whatever it is they do. Michael called Antonio's cell phone to let him know we would be ready to be picked up at 10:00 a.m., which worked out perfect because it would take him about an hour and a half to bring the Zodiac back over to Marina Grande to pick us up. Breakfast was perfect and relaxing, really setting the stage for the wonderful day we had waiting ahead. Since Antonio seemed to know the island well, Michael suggested we have him take us to the Blue Grotto then on to see any other highlights he could recommend. I always find if you have locals show you the hidden highlights on a trip, you get to have even better experiences than you could ever imagine, and that's just what happened.

Antonio showed up right on time pulling the boat up to the dock while waving good morning to us just as our open-air taxi pulled in. Alto was also there to greet us again and help us into our raft, or I guess I should say, help Jackie and her luggage into the raft. With a big smile he gave Jackie a huge hug, which was very sweet but I think it creeped Jackie out just a little bit. He grabbed her around both of her knees with his tiny little hands, pushing the side of his head into her saying, "Thank you for coming to our Island, we look forward to seeing you again!" I could tell by the look on her face she was about to tell him it was time for him to let go of her legs already and take a hike, or better yet, follow the yellow brick road. And I would probably have to agree with her. That little island novelty was sort of cute the first time, but not anymore. Especially the whole touching thing; he shouldn't be hugging women, or anyone for that matter, who is crotch height to his head. In addition guests should be treated the same way as any respectable pole dancer—no touch!

As we pulled away from the marina heading west toward the Grotta Azzura, Antonio said he wanted to take us to his favorite swimming spot. It was a small inlet only accessible by water while protected on three sides. Antonio stopped the boat and told us to go ahead and jump in, explaining we were in the perfect spot to swim. Distracted by the sheer beauty of the surroundings we almost forgot to look at the details, which in this case would have been a disaster. Jackie had taken off her cover up, and we were just getting ready to jump in when Michael told us to stop. Looking down into the dark clear blue water he showed us what we did not see, thousands of small purple jellyfish. "Go ahead," Antonio said, "it's not a problem, jump in." *Are you kidding?* I thought, I've dealt with painful purple on my face before from a dermatological condition that took a year of daily doses of Accutane to get over with lifelong side effects. I sure as heck now didn't need to throw my whole body into a sea of purple that sting unless of course I wanted to legitimately adopt and sing the anthem of the Tin Man, "If I only had a brain…" Needless to say we opted out and told Antonio to go ahead to the Blue Grotto; we were not going to partake in the purple passion of Capri.

When we arrived at the Blue Grotto there were about ten to fifteen different white row boats beyond the private passenger boats taking people in and out of the passageway into the cave. Surprisingly in what looks like total confusion is complete organization. As the tide ebbs and flows in and out of the opening to the cave it dictates when the boats can enter. Since you can only enter on the official boats, you have to wave them over. A gondolier will then paddle over to your boat, take your money, help you get onto their boat and then you get in line. When it's your turn, you wait for the water to rush out of the cave as the gondolier tells you to lay down flat on your back while he quickly grabs a hold of a big heavy chain that's attached to the rock and hurriedly pulls the boat under a three foot clearance into another world. This experience is definitely a moment in time, where within seconds time seems to slow down so fast it almost stops. It is a grotto of magnificent unparalleled natural beauty. The cave is black inside yet gently lit by the breathless beauty of sunlight shining through natural rock formations under the water, turning the water to a bright and clear cobalt blue. The gondoliers start singing "Oh Sole Mio" ("my sunshine") in unison as they row around the large grotto, making you feel like you're the star in a Disney animated feature.

BLUE GROTTO CAPRI

It was now after one o'clock by the time we left the Blue Grotto, and all three of us were starting to get hungry for lunch.

We asked Antonio what we should do, if we should head on back or try to find something on the island. He told us he had already made reservations for us at his favorite lunch spot on Capri, La Fontelina. So if it was okay with us he would take us there then onto the Green Grotto before we returned to Positano. Since we weren't on any real schedule, we thought his ideas sounded great, so to La Fontelina we went. When you arrive at La Fontelina by boat you have to off-load onto a small rock platform at the edge of La Fontelina beach club. The restaurant sits above the cliff over rough-hewn rocks which hug the sea below giving you a view of the rustically elegant beach club offering natural swimming holes carved into the rocks made up of multiple hues of turquoise sea water. Blue and white striped umbrellas dot the rocky hillside as they cover white lounging chairs in this perfectly secluded slice of paradise. It is known as one of the most beautiful beach clubs in Italy, not to mention one of the most exclusive. And the private yachts—or should I say private mega yachts—anchored out in the ocean just beyond quietly yet boldly suggest you will be mingling with bathing-clad elite. But the best part for me is how all this is casually balanced by each staff member, offering every patron the warmest of welcomes and the finest food. The establishment is a family affair of several generations gone by. And as you sit under the thatched roof pergola of the restaurant watching the ways of the entertaining wait staff, you can quickly tell it's a fun and happy place. Chef Mario, as they call him, had prepared a number of tempting off-menu treats, so while we relaxed and looked out at the waves gently lapping against the Faraglioni rocks before breaking on the islands sunny shores, I thought it would be the perfect time to order a glass of their legendary iced sangria, a chilled white wine filled with fresh slices of the islands local peaches. I think my pallet was officially starting to mature; I couldn't wait to tell my brother. Michael ordered a *paranza* for the table paired with a red wine for him and Jackie

LA FONTELINA BEACH CLUB

as a starter before we moved on to one of their homemade fresh pasta dishes. I could have sat there all day getting lost indulging myself in the pure relaxed and understated elegant surroundings, but we still had more to do. Knowing we had to force ourselves to get up and leave, we walked down the path from the restaurant to the boat landing looking out over the water for Antonio. But as we looked out over the water we could not find Antonio or even our raft for that matter.

There had to be at least fifty small rafts and medium-sized skiffs, but where had he gone? Standing on the rock ledge, Jackie caught the attention of a man who ran a twenty-foot old- fashioned wooden boat hopper for the restaurant. He waved us over asking us if we needed help. We told him we were trying to find our boat but couldn't see it. "No problem, I'm Agapeto, get in and I will take you to find it," he said. So with that we got in as he helped Jackie while staring had her impossibly huge diamond studded cross hanging from her neck and Michael's diamond and sapphire Rolex that flashed in the sun. Oh and my jewelry was a rubber watch. I'm sure it made me look like the friend. "What does your yacht look like?" he asked after looking at Jackie. Oh no, I thought, I know exactly what he is thinking. He thinks we have one of those large super yachts out there. This is so embarrassing, what are we going to do? We were thinking he was going to just take us out among the small boats to try and find Antonio as I had a feeling he was probably lying down in the bottom of our raft sleeping in the sun. We had not been looking long before Antonio miraculously woke up and started waving and yelling to us while standing in the raft trying to get our attention. Of course, I wanted to ignore him but he was our ride. And with that Michael said, "Oh there he is over there" as he pointed over to Antonio. With a confused look on Agapeto's face, I knew I had to say something, so I told him that was Antonio our driver, and our yacht must have moved around the corner, so if he could just take us to Antonio that would be fine. Jackie pulled out a healthy tip from her change purse as we loaded onto our raft, and I prayed he didn't follow us.

GREEN GROTTO CAPRI

Next on our stop was the Grotta Verde or Green Grotto. Who knew grottos came in so many colors. Just on Capri alone there are blue, green, red, and white, with each one offering a different experience. The Green Grotto is different from the blue and not just because it's green. It's an open cave grotto that you can swim through. Starting at the beginning you swim from the open ocean through a system of open and arched rock formations that give a bright emerald green composite effect due to the blue light reflected and transmitted from the water, playing upon the yellowish-hued sides and roof of the open caves. The water below you as well as the ocean floor is also a bright emerald green. Antonio decided to stop the raft so we could jump out and swim through; he told us he would pick us up on the other side. It sounded really exciting to me and to Michael both, but when we looked over at Jackie she now looked like a female version of Green Lantern. Her face was limey green, and it wasn't from the reflection. She was quickly getting sick from the bobbing and weaving of the raft sitting there. We told her to jump in with us, it would make her feel better, but that wasn't going to happen. I noticed she was starting to do some kind of a weird reverse swallow thing with her mouth, which is never a good sign when someone is getting sick. It was best they take off to get some wind in her face before her lunch of seafood became just that.

Michael and I then quickly jumped in the water and told Antonio we would meet them on the other side, and I was so glad we decided to jump in. Then off they went while we swam toward the grotto. The water was so salty it kept you afloat without much work, which made the experience much more enjoyable as we lightly treaded, floated and swam with others through the grotto. What a beautiful gift from nature for all of us to enjoy without having to use a theme park fast pass. Once we got through to the other side, Antonio and Jackie were there waiting. Jackie looked a lot better so I didn't even need to ask if she fed the fish, if you know what I mean. We got in the raft and drove back to the beach in Positano.

Since it was our last night in the Amalfi, we decided to dress up and go to a more formal dinner. Michael was in linen pants and a white shirt, all tan with perfectly styled James Bond hair and movie star looks while turning the heads of every woman in town. Jackie, on the other hand, was even tanner, dressed in a see-through black gauzy skirt and low cut tank, turning the heads of all the men in town as they tried to see what she claimed was only an illusion, and maybe it was in the right light but I was too tired for her magic shows. I just wanted to have a nice dinner and see if we could get any more clues or even an ending to her story.

We chose Le Sirenuse as our dining destination. It is a beautiful scarlet red hotel with white shuttered trim that sits above the ocean on the cliff like a center jewel in a crown. And since a Sirenuse is another name for a mermaid, they make sure to find very interesting ways to use the image as an accessory. Our table was perfectly appointed out on the veranda under a dusk sky of silvery blue. Sitting there we watched from above as the beachside town came alive for another night with its enchanting strings of café lights gently swaying in the warm soft breeze of the ocean. What a perfect way to wrap up a perfect day with a ribbon of memories from one of the most enchanted places on earth.

CHAPTER 10

When in Rome

The next morning we awoke early to have breakfast and prepare for our departure to Rome.
Christiano was scheduled to pick us up at 10:00
a.m. to take us back to the train station in Naples for an
11:30 departure. Just as scheduled, he was there right on
time pulling up to the town square in his big blue Mercedes.
After getting our entire luggage tower loaded into the car, he
handed each of us a chilled water bottle, gave a big smile and
told us how great it was to be together again. He was such a
nice guy.

Michael and Jackie sat in the back while I sat in the front,
and with the air condition on full blast, we drove through the

hillsides of Amalfi secured and relaxed. *I don't want to get on a train*, I thought, *this is too nice. I wonder if he will take us to Rome. Hmm*, I thought, *how can we make that happen? I know, I'll remind Jackie about the pick pocket incident while casually suggesting how dirty the train was.* Turning my head around I saw both of them completely sprawled out in the back as if they were being toured by their staff in the front seat. *Oh this is going to be easier than I thought*, I said to myself. Then I looked at both of them with sort of a disgusted look on my face and asked if they thought the train on the way down was sort of dirty, not to mention the whole gypsy thing. "Oh," Jackie said, "it wasn't only terrible, it was unsafe. I honestly wish we didn't even have to get out of this car!"

"Well", Michael said, "maybe we don't, Christiano how much would it be to have you take us to Rome, and would you be willing to do it?"

"Let me make a quick call," Christiano said, and within two minutes he was off the phone with a smile on his face not only telling us he could do it, but that it would be a flat rate of $300. The three of us took all of a half-second vote as Jackie sipped from her chilled water bottle in the back seat as if she was Miss Daisy with her pinky finger out. She handed me four hundred dollar bills from her purse while shaping the words with her mouth, "It's a tip." I gave the bills to Christiano, I didn't have to say a word; the money talked for itself. He then gently applied more pressure to the gas pedal, picking up significant speed on the highway heading straight for Rome. It ended up to be a great decision to splurge and have Christiano drive us all the way through. Taking in the views of the countryside and learning from him about the region was truly fascinating, making for an informative yet relaxing experience. Not to mention we didn't have to schlep Jackie's luggage around. Just that was worth the four hundred dollars!

Entering through the walls of Rome otherwise known as the Eternal City, I could quickly tell why they say Rome wasn't built in a day. This is a city of vast history and architecture, heavily mixed with structural remnants and ruins of the past that stand to remind you of Rome's quest to be the center of the world. But today most of that is a backdrop to a city changed by the cultural hands of time, where designer stores, bobbled boutiques, and fashion houses lure you in with a kaleidoscope of colorful window displays offering the best there is to those that can afford it, while less than a mile away lays a different kaleidoscope of color, Vatican City. It's a city state all to its own where religious vows and apostolic following define its day to day order and existence, a place where authority of the church goes beyond its walls to all those who take a vow to the Catholic faith. The smallest country in the world governing over the largest religious population in the world of over a billion people, a place I couldn't wait to explore.

"Oh, Michael, I dropped my sunglasses," Jackie said as two excited bellman almost collided heads trying to pick them up for her at the same time. We were now at our hotel, the St. Regis in Rome. In 1894 Swiss hotelier Cesar Ritz opened the Grand Hotel as the most elegant hotel of Italy with Auguste Escoffier as its first chef and Lina Cavalieri as the establishments flower girl. Walking through the grand entrance I could only imagine dining at one of the white linen draped tables listening to Lina sing *Fedora* in her famous operatic voice with Caruso to the Umberto Giordano opera, while enjoying Escoffier's famed creation, the Peach Melba. We had just walked through the doors into another kind of world, a world where the cultural, economic, and social revolving points of Italy reside.

ST. REGIS ROME

"Please, follow me," the impeccable black and white clad front desk assistant said to us upon our arrival while carrying a dozen red-tipped yellow roses. "I will be showing you to your rooms, my name is Andrea." With everyone dressed formally in black and white, I knew Jackie should feel right at home. Black and white always seem to be her go-to colors, and on this trip I was going to make sure I encouraged her whenever I could to mix it up, and no I didn't mean to fifty shades of gray. For her the upside of dressing that way was she would always be ready for either a funeral or a wedding at any given moment. Although it was becoming increasingly impossible to deny the fact that we were in a city flooded with nuns, and with her big gold and diamond cross relentlessly swinging from her neck, she could easily be mistaken for one of them while at the same time looking like the outcast who rebelled against the vow of poverty—probably not a good idea. So this opportunity presented itself to be an excellent launching pad to start her eagerly awaiting couture collection of color. Why wait for Paris?

"Please allow me," Andrea said as he opened the door to Jackie's room gesturing for us to walk in with him following close behind. Setting the dozen long-stemmed red-tipped yellow roses into a crystal vase onto the center table of her room, he continued to open another door to what would be the second room of a luxury suite. There was a knock on the door, our luggage arrived, and while the bellmen arranged our luggage as perfectly as the roses delivered to Jackie, I looked over at Michael and said, "I think roses could be trending"

"Really," he said, "whatever gives you that idea?" as he acted like he never saw them.

"Well," I said, "this is the second time roses have shown up, and I noticed a small white card secured to a clear plastic stick inside the roses when we were walking up to the room with Andrea. The card had a heart drawn on it with a big *S* underneath of it. I don't think the *S* stands for St. Regis."

Michael looked at me and said, "The best thing to do is just ignore it, don't say anything, and we'll wait and see if she says anything to us. I mean who knows maybe she is trying to make one of us jealous." *Of what*, I thought, *Samuele standing around with his chest puffed out putting his hands through his hair like he's king of the forest every time Jackie walks in a room? I don't think so.*

While putting all our stuff away, we decided to take the next few daylight hours we had left and go out and explore the city. The three of us agreed it would be a good idea to change into shorts, tee shirts and our trek sandals because it was hot, and I don't mean "oh I need to fan my armpits hot"—it was Africa hot! I didn't realize how the warm air in Rome gets trapped between the buildings, and then you add that to the heat created by the sun reflecting off of the cobblestone streets, and you feel like you're only one hit with a eucalyptus *venik* away from a Russian *banya*. This is why I didn't understand why Jackie appeared minutes later for our next exploration in heels, tight skinny jeans, and a tube top. Was she determined to squeeze the last bit of water out of her system in this heat for her upcoming couture purchases? Was she self-imposing fashion pressure on herself, or had she just forgotten how hot it was outside and what we had all just agreed to do as she stood in an air-conditioned room? I decided to go with the probability of the last choice, so I reminded her and told her it would be totally justified if she took off the jeans and put on a skirt or shorts. I thought changing out the shoes would then be obvious to her, but it wasn't.

She was now standing in her room in shorts, the same impossibly high heels and the tube top, oh and the diamond cross, which I guess with this outfit was supposed to cover her multitude of fashion sins. *I can't help out anymore*, I thought. *Why am I so concerned about her anyway? She's the one that's going to have to walk in those shoes, not me.* Being obviously irritated I looked at Michael and quietly said, "What is wrong with her? She is never going to make it, those shoes, look at her in there."

He looked at me as if he was serious and said, "Before criticizing someone, walk a mile in their shoes."

"That would be both good and bad," I said. "The good is I'd be a mile away, the bad is I'd have her shoes, which now that I think about it, I'll probably have in my hand anyway once she decides her feet hurt and she has to buy a new pair." *Oh that's it! She wants another pair of shoes*, I thought.

"I'm ready" she said walking through the doorway. "Do you think this will be better?"

"You look great," Michael said. "Let's get going." I walked a few steps behind them down the cobblestone streets for safety just in case she fell. I didn't want to be in the way if Michael had to do a romance novel "heroin dive bomb catch" since her legs were wobbling like a Fiat with two diagonal flat tires, but I could tell she felt pretty, so I guess that's all that really mattered. After taking in a few shops her feet started to hurt. Actually "unexpectedly hurt" was how she put it, and we were all getting hungry anyway, not to mention it was way past the melting point outside even in the late afternoon. So Michael suggested we beat the heat and find an air-conditioned restaurant to have an early dinner and relax in until the sun had set. We ended up at Gioia Mia. The food was wonderful and authentic and made for an even more interesting evening when we discovered there was another pleasure besides the food that had been served there at the beginning of the twentieth century. The restaurant served as an antechamber to the upper rooms of the building filled with beautiful women who practiced one of the oldest professions in the world, and I'm not talking about cooking! Michael ordered the lamb *osso bucco* style, Jackie had ravioli with vodka sauce, and I ordered simple marinara spaghetti. I wasn't feeling very exotic; the heat had stripped me of almost everything but my appetite. I guess if I had been there a hundred years earlier, my loss could have made for an equally interesting and eventful evening.

While we relaxed and ate, Jackie mentioned she had always wanted to go to the Trevi fountain and toss in a coin. "Let's do it," Michael said. "I know right where it is; actually it's not far from where we are now."

"Do you mind if we stop by a shoe store on our way so I can buy a pair of flats?" I looked at her in her tube top and wanted to inform her that she was far from having a set of flats as she sat there looking like she was surprised her feet hurt!

"Of course not," Michael said, "We've spent this much money for comfort on this trip there's no need to be uncomfortable now."

"I would really appreciate it," she said. "Oh and do either of you know the legend of the Trevi?"

"I do," Michael blurted out as if he was going to continue on by saying. "Pick me! Pick me!" He was in luck because neither Jackie nor I knew the legend, so he was picked and would now be our tour guide. "We'll," he said, "There is a long-standing tradition about throwing coins in the Trevi Fountain. The original legend says if you throw a coin into the fountain with your right hand over your left shoulder, you will ensure a return trip to Rome." He then went on to tell us about an updated version of the legend that says if you throw one coin it means a trip to Rome, a second coin leads to a new romance, and a third coin leads to marriage. I watched Jackie's eyes as if she was counting while he was telling us the story. I better make sure we get enough change from the waiter before we leave I thought; I have a suspicion more than one coin is going to be tossed tonight.

The sun had set and the lights of Rome had been turned on. Vespas whizzed by us as we walked down the street, weaving in and out of pedestrians and traffic like runners in the Bull Run of Navarra. It made the search for Jackie's shoes a stressful proposition, so we hired a cab to save us time and energy. He took us to the ideal shoe store where Jackie found eight more pairs of shoes, which meant I got four new bags to carry. He then dropped us off at the Trevi fountain where we treated ourselves to fresh Italian gelato as we sat by the cool splashing water of the fountain, the biggest fountain in the entire city of Rome, watching hopeful people of all ages toss in their coins, believing in a dream.

"Well, do you think it's time?" Jackie said excitedly.

"For what?" I said as Michael and I sat there looking at her with a look of question on our faces.

TREVI FOUNTAIN ROME

"To throw our coins in the fountain?" she continued to say as she started digging in her change purse for euros. We told her yes, and then we all got up and walked over in front of the middle section of the fountain so I could get both her and Michael's pictures with the fountain positioned directly behind them as they threw in their coins. Michael went first tossing in only one coin. Jackie threw in a handful of six. As I stood there watching them rain down from the sky. I thought to myself maybe the additional three coins were to secure a backup plan. You know, just in case it doesn't work out with one guy, then she would have more potential chances it would with the next. If I was advising her, I would have told her to just go ahead and dump in her whole change purse! I went next and also decided to only toss in one coin. Since I wasn't in the frame of mind right then to allow the toss of more than one coin to potentially mess up the future I was working so hard to regain.

We got some great pictures and then continued on for the rest of Michael's tour. He had several other fountains he wanted to show us that were within walking distance of the Trevi, now that Jackie had on appropriate shoes. Each fountain was an architectural phenomenon all to its own. True art at its finest, brought alive by the waters of life from aqueducts within the city feeding the fountains by elevation and gravity combined. They are the gathering places for people at night, sustaining a different kind of life. One filled with people exchanging stories, laughter, and music in the breeze of the evening being cooled by the waters of a fountain.

The next morning we awoke early since it was our only full day in Rome. We had a lot to see and do in a very short time frame in addition to the long awaited tour of the Scavi I had scheduled with the Vatican several months earlier for that day. I was excited jumping into the shower to get ready as quickly as I could since Michael and Jackie had finished getting ready before me. When I got out of the shower and came into the room to get my clothes, I saw Michael sitting at the desk doing something on his iPhone while Jackie was making sling shots out of my underwear. She had taken it upon herself to make a unilateral decision about my white briefs saying they were passé, not sexy, completely old man and needed to be thrown out, literally.

She had opened the large floor-to-ceiling French doors in my room that looked out over the rooftop garden eight stories below and was standing there flinging my under-wear into the air one after another decorating the garden. "What are you doing?" I yelled in shock. Laughing she said, "Oh I saw your clothes laid out over the chair and your underwear on top of your pants, I couldn't believe you wear *tighty whities*. As your friend I decided you don't need these anymore, you need to get new underwear, something sex-ier, younger, and something more you." Why did she even care? And who made her fashion police captain in charge of the Underwear Division anyway? Not only did I not find it the least bit funny that all of my underwear were gone, but I would now be going commando for the first time in my life! Would people know? Would they be staring and talking? I didn't know. I felt vulnerable and weird like I had a big dirty secret, no pun intended. I had to tell myself over and over it was all in my head and that God understood and would not care that I had to go commando in the Sistine Chapel. I then rationalized in my mind that Michelangelo's paintings and sculptures would for that matter make me look like an extremely modest offender. So with that I went back into the bathroom and got dressed, having to change out of my white pants, for obvious reasons, and into a pair of khakis.

As the three of us left the room and walked down the grand stairs of the hotel for breakfast, I was so self-conscious. I thought about those high society events where the parents come down the staircase into the ballroom to present their child to the world as officially eligible to date, usually referred to as a debutant ball. But in this case I felt like Michael and Jackie were presenting me at more of a *beautillion* ball. "Welcome to the ballroom, are you joining us this morning for the buffet?" the host said as we entered the room full of tables, ice sculptures, and food. Really I thought, he would have to say welcome to the ballroom!

"Yes, I think we are," Michael and Jackie said at the same time laughing, "We have a very big day ahead of us." I knew right then my best chance to buy underwear in the next twenty four hours would be if for some weird reason they were being sold in a shoe store.

By the time we finished breakfast, we only had a few hours before the necessary check in time at St. Peters for the Scavi Tour. And since it was my first time in Rome I wanted to make sure I at least got to see the top ten things you're not supposed to miss when you go. Michael and Jackie had been many times before, so I wasn't sure if they would be interested in hiring a cab and going with me. I figured it would only take me an hour by car to see everything I wanted to see, and then that would allow us the perfect amount of time to get over to Vatican City a little early, get checked in, and relax for a few minutes before the tour began.

Both of them said they wanted to go with me, so they quickly helped me put a list together of all of the places we needed to try and see. We then asked the bellman to please call a car for us.

When we got into the car our driver asked us how much time we had. I handed him the list that Michael and Jackie helped me with and told him these were the places we would like to see, but we also needed him to drop us off at St. Peters in an hour and a half. He said no problem he would do his best, then went on to say if he could just quickly stop the car

COLISEUM OF ROME

for us to take pictures rather than having to park for all of us to get out, then we would have a better chance of seeing everything on my list. He asked me to sit on the right side of the car since it would be easier for him to approach the ruins, sites, and points of interest from that side of the car for my pictures. Luckily I had listened to my inner voice that morning and popped a Dramamine before I left the room. I had a feeling there was a high probability we would be ending up in a taxi at some point in the morning because we were on such a compressed time frame. Definitely not a way to see Rome, but with the toss of the one coin from the night before, I knew I would be back again to see it all the right way.

The first drive-by photo shoot was of the Coliseum, which dates back to 72 AD. It was so fascinating to see the architecture of that era still standing and preserved. I think that would win the prize for the oldest and most well-pre-served object I had ever seen or been introduced to in my life, if you don't count the person in front of me in the buffet line at breakfast. Next on the list was the Pantheon, built by the orders of Hadrian between 118 AD and 125 AD and still to this day the original bronze entry doors stand, greeting all those who enter. It was amazing to me that antiquities such as those doors just sit out openly accessible to the general public. If it was in the United States those doors would be in a museum under armed guard.

Jackie's addition to the list was the next stop, the Roman Forum. Big surprise since among other things it was the major shopping center for Ancient Rome. Oh and speaking of shopping, the Forum ended up to be our last stop on the tour. Jackie had just remembered she didn't bring a shoulder covering with her for our tours of holy sites, which meant we had to go shopping. For the sake of time our driver suggested he go ahead and take us over to Vatican City so we wouldn't be late while still giving us enough time for Jackie to find a cover up. Although different from what I needed, I was still secretly hopeful.

Driving into Vatican City can't be described in the same awe inspiring way as being there and seeing it with your own eyes. I guess the first word that comes to mind is "powerful" and on so many levels. As our driver stopped and let us out of the car I was actually happy our sightseeing experience with him had been cut short. First because I was out of the car into fresh air and on foot, and second because from the moment you step out you realize just how much there really is to see. Michael explained to us the layout of the Vatican as we stood there in Vatican Square. He highlighted for me the different buildings, the Pope's Apartment, where certain religious ceremonies take place. And even though I had seen it all on television before, it makes it so much different when all of your five senses get to be involved on a tour.

"Look over there," Michael said as he pointed to a street vending cart parked the equivalent of two blocks away under an archway connecting to the Vatican wall. Turning around we saw multitudes of scarves in every color blowing in the breeze as if there was an official celebration in play, or perhaps it signified the official welcoming center into the city. "Let's walk over," he said, "I'm sure you'll have a pretty good chance of finding at least one scarf there, Jackie." I had to finally relent and agree that even though I needed underwear, scarves where a much better visual than hundreds of pairs of underwear flying in the breeze. Michael helped Jackie pick out a long and wide baby blue cotton summer scarf to wrap around her shoulders. It looked really nice next to her dark hair, deep tan, white tank top and long white gauze skirt, well at least until she stood in the path of direct sunlight.

While standing in the colonnade waiting for me to check in for the Scavi tour, Michael and Jackie struck up a conversation with one of the Swiss guards. Actually I think it was probably Jackie, as she stood there in the hot sunlight when she was less than two feet from the shade. After I finished checking us in and turned around to join them, I walked out the door to find her standing there lit up from the back right through the front of her dress showing a pair of skimpy black lace underwear in all of its glory. Are you kidding me? Who would ever do that, wear black lace underwear with a sheer white skirt? Oh, that's right, what was I thinking? Black and white are her go to colors. *Hmm,* I thought, *and she was so worried about making sure her shoulders were covered to enter a sacred place?* No wonder the number of Swiss Guards increased from one to three within a matter of minutes; they obviously thought she needed additional protection as I watched them give her more attention to detail than she had given herself, or so it looked.

Our tour guide Anna showed up right on time through the gates located on the Via Paolo as did the additional six people that would be taking the tour with us. Once we were all together and introduced, she let us know absolutely no photography could be taken in the necropolis and that the area we would be entering was temperature controlled for preservation purposes and would be highly humid. She then asked us to follow her as we started to make our walking decent into the lowest depths beneath St. Peters Basilica. With the push of a secret code on a secure key pad, the clear glass panel shielding the entrance like a Star Trek space ship door, slid open then quickly and securely closed behind us.

Having to walk closely next to our guide so we could hear every word she said was necessary since she didn't have a microphone and the acoustics were unforgiving. Walking deeper into the softly lit darkness under head-height brick archways, we followed an ancient road that guided the path of our tour. Undoubtedly this was the same road that once guided the feet of the original Disciples of Christ. The tour had now begun. A tour I also want to take you on.

The Tour

You are now standing underneath the largest church of the Catholic Faith, St. Peter's Basilica. This is a church that has become famous around the world as the epicenter of that faith, a place which holds priceless treasures validating the history of mankind. And out of all of these treasures the most

precious possession of them all are the bones of St. Peter, otherwise known as his relics. And today you will be seeing the bodily

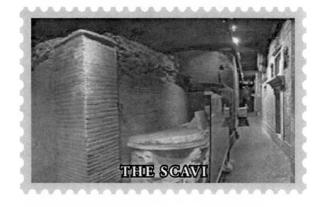

THE SCAVI

remains of this original disciple of Christ. He was the disciple who confessed his faith in Jesus upon meeting him, then denied him on the night of his betrayal, but confessed his faith in him again after the resurrection. Peter was the disciple to whom Christ spoke the words, "I also say to you that you are Peter, and upon this rock I will build My church, and the gates of Hades will not overpower it."

After the ascension of Christ, Peter continued on with his life preaching to all those he encountered for over three decades before finally being killed by the Romans. The relics you will be seeing today were thought to be buried beneath the main altar of St. Peter's Basilica, but how far down no one knew for sure. In 1968 the relics were finally identified, and the tour today will tell us the story of what happened over the previous two thousand years.

History tells us that Christianity first arrived in Rome approximately forty years after the birth of Christ, which would be about ten years after the death and resurrection of Jesus. Christianity was a small religious group that had sprung out of Judaism, and both were a persecuted group in Rome at the time. In 64 AD there was a great fire in Rome; this fire was thought to be set by Nero, who was in control and reigning over Rome at the time. It is believed he was crazy and self-centered, and those were two of the main factors that led him to want to burn down the city so that he could rebuild his own. Blame for the fire was cast onto Christians, and in its aftermath the first wave of Christian martyrdom and persecution had started in the Roman Empire.

Peter and Paul had already arrived in Rome and were residing there during this time. And because of their high visibility as two of the great apostles of Christ living in Rome, they were set up to be public targets for persecution. It is known that St. Paul was beheaded outside the city after his death sentence appeal was denied by Cesar. They claimed that since he was a citizen of Rome he was able to be given a more humane death. But St. Peter was not a Roman Citizen, so he was given death by crucifixion, which was known to be the cruelest death in the Empire at the time. History tells us that St. Peter chose to be crucified upside down as he did not want to be killed in the same position that his Lord and Savior Jesus had died.

Peter was executed in what was known at the time as Nero's circus, which was adjacent to Vatican Hill.

On the side of the hill was a necropolis where people would build elaborate tombs for members of their families who had passed on.

At the center of the circus was the obelisk that you see today standing in St. Peter's Square, brought to Rome by Caligula, a Roman Emperor whose religion was Roman paganism. It is believed that the obelisk was one of the final things St. Peter saw before he died.

As a condemned criminal he did not have the right to a proper burial, but instead he would be left on the cross in public view as a symbol to what could happen if you challenge Roman authority. But somehow the Christians of that time were able to get possession of his body and buried his remains in a grave known as a poor man's grave. Since the burial site was known to be a marshy area, they had to dig a grave in a design that would keep his body from washing away in either heavy rains or a flood. So they dug a trench for his grave, surrounded it with a small retaining wall, and then put on a covering of six large tiles in the design of a tent.

Over the next 250 years persecution of Christians continued in the Roman Empire, but even during this time Christians made sure that the grave of Peter did not go into neglect. In fact at about the time of 150 AD Christians erected a grave marker over his grave in the shape of a large simple trophy. It wasn't until Constantine the first and Licinius, who controlled the Balkans, met in Milan and agreed to change policies towards Christians, did the persecutions subside with what is known as the Edict of Milan. Over the next two hundred years walls were added to either side of the Trophy, with one of them still standing today. The wall became known as the Graffiti Wall because of its defacing over time by Greek and Latin graffiti vandals. By the time Christianity was legalized in the Roman Empire, Peter's gravesite had dramatically changed from that of his original burial.

As emperor of Rome (306 to 337 AD), Constantine decided he wanted to build what would become known as the original St. Peter's Basilica on the Vatican Hill. With its dedication in the year 326 AD the trophy was also presented as the centerpiece of the sanctuary within the Basilica. The Trophy was put into a box of marble and porphyry, which is a hard igneous rock containing fine grained crystals usually reddish in color.

Over time, renovations would take place that included building large altars directly over the grave of St. Peter. In the sixteenth century the Basilica we see today replaced the original Basilica, positioning the main altar high above all previous altars. Hundreds of years passed with a traditional acceptance that the tomb of St. Peter was in fact directly below the high Papal Altar. But it wasn't until survey work was done in the 1940s, in the grotto level of the Basilica, was history confirming evidence found to support the facts of what had previously been held up only by tradition.

Pope Pius XII was the current pope of the time and he appointed two Jesuit priests to lead a top secret excavation of the new found ancient necropolis. He also made it a requirement that all excavations and work be done at night so that the chances of anyone being alerted would be lessened. But as fate would have it, a member of the clergy who was also overseeing the excavations, Monsignor Kaas, was not happy about the way the project was being handled and felt that newly discovered bones were not being treated with the respect they deserved. So he took it upon himself to get involved and would send his workers into the excavation site to remove the bones and put them into storage. This unilateral decision to intervene in sound archaeological work would end up causing major and unnecessary setbacks in this highly anticipated discovery process.

Excavators in 1950 were able to secure permission once again to dig. The digging would take place under the main alter, and their findings would prove to be a step forward, well sort of. They found the Poor Man's Grave, but what they also found inside were the bones of three human skeletons, one of them being a woman, along with an assortment of animal bones. They decided their work was a failure and stopped excavations.

After the death of Monsignor Kass, Professor Margherita Guarducci discovered the relics by chance that Monsignor Kass had previously put away in storage. These were bones that had originally been found in a hollow niche in the Graffiti Wall several decades earlier. Upon examination of the bones they were found to be of a sixty- to seventy-year-old man with a large build.

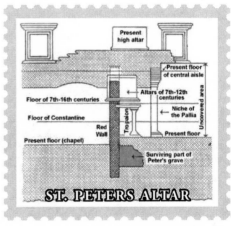

ST. PETERS ALTAR

Bones from all major parts of the body except for the feet were there, and the bones were covered in soil, which matched the soil found in the Poor Man's Grave. This soil is said to be an uncommon soil for the region. Several additional defining factors to the confirmation and the validity of the bones were given to the fact that the bones were seen to be covered in a purple dye reserved only for the Emperor and high level Roman officials and a small piece of wall next to the place where the bones were found was marked in Greek, "Peter is within."

On June 26, 1968, Pope Paul VI announced that the relics of St. Peter had been discovered. The relics were displayed publicly for the first time on November 24, 2013 by Pope Francis after the closing of the Year of Faith Mass. The relics of St. Peter have since been placed in a series of small clear boxes and put back into the original Graffiti Wall niche, now confirming their location directly underneath the main Papal Altar of St. Peter's Basilica.

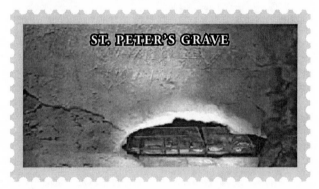
ST. PETER'S GRAVE

"This completes our tour of the Scavi," Anna said as we stood as a group in front of the relics of St. Peter. "I would like to now invite all of you to join in with me as I say the Lord's Prayer." Everyone in the group seemed to know and recite the prayer; it was a very moving experience, standing with a group of nine other people within the silence and depths of the earth, protected from the outside world in front of the relics of a man who was said to have been personally touched by God and who personally touched God himself.

"What should we do now?" Jackie asked once we emerged from the tour. Looking at her in her baby blue wrap, I thought it would be best to get as much mileage out of her approved "sacred look" as we could, so I suggested we see as many holy sites in the area as possible. Michael then said we should see the Sistine Chapel next, and we all agreed. Walking over to the entrance of the chapel, they told me about their past experiences there and sort of what to expect. But when we walked in the experience was nothing like what they had described. The two entry guards who are supposed to check for appropriate clothing and give you a brief outline of the rules before you go in were not only completely oblivious to who was coming and going, but also to what was going on inside. These two guys just sloppily sat at their post in their uniforms talking to each other like they were exhausted from a hard night of partying and dancing on boxes the night before at the local disco.

When we walked into the chapel it was packed with people so tight you could hardly walk through. The typical young groups of Asian tourists were there with their cameras taking and posing for photos even though it is prohibited. And since most of the artwork you want to see is on the ceiling a lot of people are walking around aimlessly with their heads tilted back running into others doing the same thing. One couple I accidentally ran into didn't seem to mind as they had decided it was their moment to start making out with each other, kissing deeper than the meaning of the artwork they obviously didn't understand. When I said excuse me, they just took a few steps over in the opposite direction, never break-

SISTINE CHAPEL

ing the seal of their lips. It would have made a perfect ad for super glue.

Looking up at the ceiling again, Michael tried to explain to us the sequencing of the famous mural, and right when he got to the part where Adam is touching God, a huge fat man in a sweaty cabana shirt carrying a nylon camera bag over his shoulder shoved right into me. Almost falling over, I quickly took a couple of steps in the opposite direction to keep my balance without knocking Jackie over. A person yelled from below me. I looked down to find a dwarf woman yelling at me to watch where I'm stepping. "I'm sorry," I said, "I got pushed by that big guy right there." She didn't seem to care as she continued on yelling at me that I had big feet. Knowing my feet are average size, I realized they probably looked big to her, but then again I'm sure most things do. I tried to be nice to her but nice didn't help; she kept yelling I stepped on her foot. I was so irritated by that point with her, the deafening sound of the crowd and the pushing and shoving I almost looked down at her and said, "Hey guess what, I'm not wearing underwear and I have three nuts," but then I looked at her even closer as her mouth was moving and saw she had the face of a squirrel, so probably not a good idea. I also didn't want to elicit even a louder scream from the dwarf woman wearing sandals with man feet, so I decided to say something to her that would be more...educational, I guess, so I said, "You know what, maybe if you didn't wear open toe puppet shoes and stayed in the gift shop where they have postcards of the artwork the same size as you, you'd be happier."

"Let's get out of here," Michael said. "This is ridiculous, those security guards aren't doing anything, I've been here multiple times, and I have never seen it this way."

"Well," I said, "maybe after the bakery bell rings for their fresh donut feeding, the guards will have the energy to stand up and do something."

"Donuts," Jackie said, "that actually sounds good. Let's get out of here and go get lunch!" Laughing we told her we were right behind her and to lead the way.

We found a great little street café with metal tables under a tent sitting in front of a large free standing fan that blew out a water mist every few seconds. It was the perfect lunch retreat offering an oasis out of the sun replete with a vast selection of salads, pastas, and gelato. After ordering several different lunch specials to share, we relaxed and got out our map to plan the rest of our last day in Rome.

After finishing lunch we walked out through St. Peter's Square and noticed a large shop filled with original tile mosaics, jewelry, and much more. All three of us decided we wanted to go in and look around so we did. Michael saw a sign at one of the jewelry counters that said any jewelry purchases made by 3 p.m. can be blessed by the pope and returned to your hotel by 10 a.m. the following morning. I knew we didn't have to check out and leave to the airport until 11 a.m. so I was really excited to get something. Since I'm not Catholic, I assumed I didn't have a patron saint, so I decided to get a gold medallion of a saint who carried my middle name. I then asked the lady at the counter if she had a St. Steven, and opening a large safe she pulled out a look book filled with clear pocketed plastic pages stuffed alphabetically in sections with all the 18K gold medallions available. Flipping through the pages we got to the *S* page, and there it was. One gold St. Stephen medallion was left. I knew it was mine, waiting for me, my memory token from the trip, and if it also got blessed by the pope and protected me then that would even be better.

"Whose phone is that ringing?" Michael said looking at Jackie and I. Checking my pocket I pulled out my phone to find it was Marie calling me. Knowing we were going to St. Peter's that day she wanted to call and hopefully catch us in time to tell us about a store we needed to try and find that had beautiful tile mosaics, jewelry, artwork, and more. I told her I thought we were already there, and sure enough we were. She was so excited and went on to ask me if I could please buy a gold medallion for her son, my nephew Peter, as he had just been confirmed, and she wanted me to have it blessed by the pope and bring it home for him. I told her she had called just in time, and I only had a few minutes to get it done since 3 p.m. was the cut off time to get purchases blessed.

Hanging up the phone I told Michael and Jackie what we needed to do. Michael went and got the same lady who had just finished helping us and asked if she would help us again, telling her we needed one more medallion for my nephew who had just been confirmed. "What name do you need the medallion to be?" she asked. I told her we needed a St. Peter to which she replied, "I have the perfect one."

"Great," I said while closely looking at it. "I'll take it."

"What would you both think if we go back to the hotel now, relax a bit in the air-conditioned room, then have an early dinner and get packed?" I asked.

"I think it's a great idea," Jackie said. "In fact, maybe we could even do a little bit of evening shopping. There were some stores close to the hotel that looked really nice I wouldn't mind checking out."

"Okay," Michael said, "let's get a cab and go back, it really is too hot to be out here."

When we arrived at the hotel, Andrea was at the front desk and called over to us. "Miss Jackie, I have a package here for you at the desk I was just getting ready to deliver to your room. Would you like to take it with you now or I can deliver it to you?" She told him she could take it with her now as she walked over to retrieve a beautifully wrapped box. We all guessed who it was from and what it could be as we walked up to the room. Jackie acted as if she had no idea, playing it off like it was probably meant for someone else and somehow got mixed up at the front desk. I told her it looked like a shoe box. I was sure someone had sent her a pair of shoes, or she bought a pair she had forgotten about. "Did you order a pair of shoes that you forgot about and have them sent to the hotel," I asked?

"No," she said as she sat down on the bed to open the box. And sure enough, there was a pair of beautiful candy pink high heels from Dolce & Gabbana nested inside. She took them out and put them on; they were the perfect size and fit like a glove. "Well, Cinderella, who's the prince charming?" I sort of jokingly said. Standing up in her shoes while looking at Michael and me as if she wanted approval, she said she had no idea. "Look in the tissue," I told her. "There has to be a card or something in there." But there wasn't. Then I noticed when she picked up the box lid a small black envelope taped to the inside. "There it is, Jackie, open it!" Carefully pulling the envelope from the tape, she opened it to find a small card with "Love Mee" written on it. What is that supposed to mean? I thought, *is it a valediction, a request from someone who wants to be chosen, or someone's initials?* And whoever wrote the card didn't capitalize the "E" and move it over, or was this code and written that way on purpose?

"Well, they're not from me," I said. "Are they from you, Michael?"

"No, they're not from me," he said. "Jackie, are they from you?" we both said.

"No, they're not from me," she answered while laughing. So the mystery of "Mee" had now begun.

All of us decided it would now be a good time to pack considering Jackie now had another pair of shoes she had to try and fit into her luggage. She called Michael in to sit on one of the luggage pieces so they could try together to get it zipped closed. And although they were successful, it was bulging at the seams. She agreed that shopping that night would probably not be a good idea, and she should just wait for Paris. I told her it would also be a good idea if she shipped some of her stuff home just to make our return trip easier for everyone, and she agreed. We called the front desk and asked them if they could take care of some shipments back to the United States for us. They were more than helpful packing everything we could talk her into sending, with the majority being eleven pairs of shoes.

We had a nice dinner by the Spanish Steps that evening topping it off with pistachio gelato sitting by the Fontana della Baraccia ("fountain of the old boat"). A perfect way to end  our last night in Rome watching people move about like the backdrop of an Édouard Manet painting brought to life. The next morning while still asleep I was awoken by a knock on the door. Realizing we had all overslept, I got up and answered the door to find Andrea standing before me. He had come to deliver the medallions, each in a blue velvet bag with an official card confirming they had been blessed by the pope.

CHAPTER 11

Dire Bonjour à Paris (Say Hello to Paris)

The hotel never told us they were still sucking in top dollar for the rooms at their self- proclaimed five-star Luxury Collection Hotel, which was getting ready to close within the next year at the tony address on Avenue George V. The pictures on the Internet were even lit well and taken at the perfect angle so as not to let on that they were closing soon. Unlike celebrity photos where you can usually tell they are old and worn even with good makeup and lighting, photos of furniture and rooms don't always offer the same visual cues. The hotel was very close to the Four Seasons Hotel, to which I will give the award for being the most beautiful and elegant in any big city in the world, but they were overbooked, and we could not get in. So we went ahead when planning this trip and booked our much anticipated stay in Paris at the hotel I will now call the "One Season Hotel."

Going through the limited inventory request I always make with room reservations such as type of beds, location of room, nonsmoking designation, breakfast options, etc. I was assured by the front desk all requests had been accommodated as they handed us the keys telling us our room was ready.

Walking down the long hallway to our room suite I couldn't help but notice all of the room service trays with wasted food sitting in front of dozens of doors. *Why are they not picking these trays up?* I thought as we continued walking down the egg scented hall. Then Michael pointed out the wall paper curling back off the wall, flapping in the breeze of the overhead air vent. "I don't know if this is going to work out," I said to Michael and Jackie.

"We'll let's make a decision once we look at the room," Michael said with the look on his face as if he already knew what was going to be on the other side of the door.

"Look at the door," Jackie gasped. "It looks like it has been kicked in and an extra dead bolt put on!" Standing there looking like we were the main characters in a Hardy Boys and Nancy Drew mystery series, I was starting to get a really weird vibe. This was the type of place where you knew you would not be sleeping alone since you would probably have to ask the bed bugs if they wouldn't mind scooting over. Michael then opened the door to our five star suite which was underwhelmingly interior designed from floor to ceiling in different shades of blue. Our "nonsmoking room" was filled with the smell of cigarette smoke; causing me to think that nonsmoking to this hotel must mean that no one is currently in the room smoking or that a fire has not just been put out and is still smoldering in your room.

Sitting down on the French blue heavy velveteen bed spread, I looked over at Michael and asked him what we were going to do. Right then Jackie came out of the bathroom as if she was going to throw up. "What's wrong?" I asked her.

"Just go in there," she said. Not one to want to go into a bathroom after someone walks out almost gagging, I did. There was a towel in the corner slightly stained, and an opened bar of soap on the sink with several hairs on it.

"That's it," I said. "We're out of here." Not knowing where we were going to go, Michael got on his phone and started searching for hotels. It would be just our luck that several big events were happening in Paris that week, and all the hotels were booked. While Michael was on the phone there was a knock on the door; it was the doorman with our luggage. I had to ask him to please return our luggage to the lobby and that we were not going to be staying at their hotel. "Oh, what is the matter," he looked confused while standing there with a broken five-star-hotel pin on his jacket lapel. I couldn't help but laugh thinking the word impossible lives everywhere in the world.

As good fortune would have it Michael was able to secure rooms for us at the Hotel Fouquet, which was only a block down the street on the corner of Avenue George V

HOTEL FOUQUET PARIS

and Avenue Des Champs-Élysées. The rooms were double the price, but with what we were sitting in as being our only other option in the city, what else could we do? It was the end of our trip; we were determined to have a good time; and if your room accommodations are not at least as nice as your home, then what's the use of going on vacation? So we paid the price and adopted a new word for the trip: "Oh Fouquet!"

"Now for the next issue, how are we going to get there?" I asked them both as we stood in the lobby looking at our luggage that was sitting outside by the bellman's desk.

"We're going to walk," Michael said.

"Really, with all of this?" I said?

"Yes, the hotel is sending a car to take the luggage down to the end of the block while we walk," he said with a big smile. Although a little embarrassing, I knew we were on our way to one of the most expensive hotels in town and there probably wasn't anything they had not seen before. "Okay, I said, let's go and say hello to Paris! We briefly waited outside for the car to arrive so we could make sure all of our luggage was in his car and accounted for. Once the driver was there we helped him identify our entire luggage collection, but when he went to pick up the last two bags, Jackie's rolling wardrobe and Michael's leather duffel bag, a large spotted cat jumped out from behind them and took off down the street. Jackie let out a quick yelp and said, "Let's get out of here!"

While at the front desk, checking into the Fouquet I noticed a distinguished-looking bald man hovering around the lobby. We didn't pay too much attention to him as we spoke to the concierge about different points of interest in the city, securing tickets for us at the famous Moulin Rouge cabaret, and last but not least, his suggestion for the best and closest luncheon spot.

He suggested we go to their street corner café as it is one of the top in the city. As we turned around to go out the door to the café, the bald man looked at us, said hello then disappeared behind a wall. Hmm, I thought that was interesting. I wonder who he is.

Seconds after arriving at the café, the maître d' sat us at the best outdoor corner table under the large red signature awning of the hotel. Real iced tea was graciously served to each of us in a tall chilled glass full of ice, which in Europe is a big deal since trying to find ice is like trying to find Jimmy Hoffa—good luck. While we relaxed and looked over the menus I heard this woman just off to the side of me say in a heavy southern Paula Dean accent, "Excuse me, do you have any mayo?" I turned around not knowing who she was talking to just in time to see the waiter look at her as if she was only four hoofs and a curly tail away from being a pig.

He was obviously now an offended Frenchman. You never want one of those for a waiter ever because they can make your meal very hard on you. This is a culture where you don't change the food that is served and if you do they take it personally. They will spend all day making a pirouette for a Melba, showing all who are lucky enough to partake that their food is their art form, a world-class master piece only fit for the finest. Flipping his head around he said he would see what he could do.

"We'll what's his problem?" the lady said. "Has he never heard of mayonnaise?" I looked at Jackie and asked her if she had a mirror in her purse. "I do, why?"

"Because the woman behind me doesn't know why the waiter is put out, I thought it might help if I handed her a mirror." When the waiter returned, he bypassed her table and came to ours. I asked him how his day was going. As he rolled his eyes I continued to tell him we would be his favorite customers of the day, and after those four words we had five-star service.

Once we finished lunch we went to the room, changed our clothes and headed out for a trip to the Louvre, one of the most famous museums in the world where the original *Mona Lisa* lives, something I had always wanted to see but had missed on my previous trips to Paris. Feeling like we were going to meet someone whom we all knew so well but had never met makes for a different kind of excitement, especially when it's a painting. Like most works of art you may have only seen through the eyes of the media, this painting turned out to be of no exception; it was bigger than life but smaller than imagined. Hanging on a wall in a bullet proof case set back several yards behind a velvet rope, there she was in the middle of the room, seeming to look at everyone at the same time no matter where you stood. A completely different experience for me than the girl I once met in an elevator in college whose eyes each went in a different direction so you didn't know for sure which one to look at when you talked to her. I would say it's somewhat different than a lazy eye although equally distracting.

This was art at its finest, the golden egg of the Louvre, but unfortunately the museum was so overcrowded it made it too hard to enjoy, so I officially renamed it the "Leavere," and that's exactly what we ended up doing.

It was the perfect day in Paris as we walked back toward the Place de la Concorde. A warm summer breeze was blowing, the sky was infinite blue punctuated with large white clouds like cotton candy gently floating high in the sky. "Does anyone want a little dessert?" Michael said. "I know the perfect place?"

Ok, we're in Paris, we're on vacation, we've just been given a dessert alert. "Are you kidding?" I said. "On this trip no means yes, and yes means yes when it comes to dessert!"

"Alright," he said, "were on our way to the wonderful world of Angelina." Walking through the sandstone archways under the chocolate colored awning of the namesake tea house, one can tell right away this is a sophisticated experience of indulgence, a chocolate and dessert tea house from 1903 that could cause Willie Wonka to rethink his chocolate recipe and business strategy. As they say, Angelina is a calm and elegant space yet ornately fragile in the presentation of their menu items. Their African hot chocolate is a blend of three different chocolates from Niger, Ghana, and Côte d'Ivoire, and when it poured from the porcelain pourer into my cup like a thick river of pudding, my knees got week and my legs started to shake like a three-year-old boy who had just discovered chocolate.

"Jouir," the waiter said as he plopped a dollop of fresh whipped cream on the top of my chocolate filled cup telling me to go ahead and stir it in as my spoon all but stood straight up on its own. He never warned me that after drinking one full cup I would be ready for a winter's hibernation.

"Are you feeling okay?" Jackie said as she looked at me giving a blank stare.

"Yes, I'm okay, it's just that my head is spinning from the sugar drop, I thought I should pick a spot and stare at it for a few minutes." Michael had ordered the signature Mont-Blanc iconic pastry that combines meringue, light whipped cream and chestnut paste vermicelli. It's basically a small choc-

olate bomb in a ramekin. And Jackie ordered the *éclair chocolat*, which is described as a seductive Choux pastry, filled with bitter dark chocolate cream with chocolate icing. I don't know if it's necessary to say, but the three of us almost walked out of there in self-induced comas. But what a way to do it! Before we left we bought three bottles of water to take with us. We knew we each needed to have a royal flush, so we started drinking the water as we turned right to walk back to our hotel. I almost suggested we should turn left instead and head toward Notre Dame so we could ask forgiveness from our glutinous sin. I guess I was hoping to indulge at Angelina's and leave with the same feelings as an adoptive mother, having all the fun without the stretch marks.

The scarlet red windows of Cartier on Avenue Des Champs-Elysees were a magnet to Jackie's feet. "Do you guys mind if we drop in real quick?" Tom never brought me here when we came to Paris, and I always wanted to buy one of their signature tri rolling rings," Jackie said with determination in her voice like no one was going to stop her now.

"Sure, let's go," Michael and I both said. "Never a better time to spend money than when you're mad at your ex-husband and high on sugar," I said as we all laughed. Walking in the door of Cartier we were instantly greeted by security guards who gave all three of us a once over as if we were the types they would have to watch out for, you know, just your garden-variety touristy troublemakers. Possibly it was because we were in shorts and tee shirts looking slightly dazed and confused from our sugar binge along with the fact that for some stupid reason we couldn't stop laughing. But in all fairness, when they stand there and look at you like laughter in a Paris jewelry store is consi-

CARTIER PARIS

dered vulgar, that makes you laugh even harder. Well at least it did us. "Can I be of assistance to you three today?" the lady said in the snug navy suite with hair pulled back tighter than the girdle of a Baptist minister's wife. "No," I said, "we're just looking right now." I could tell they didn't really want us in there disturbing the peace. They were much more into the quiet Asians who talked under their breath and answered them by blinking and bowing.

The sales people divided up following just steps behind each of us trying to look busy as if they were organizing jewels and cleaning dirty yet spotless glass cases. I knew what was up, so when I walked by the bracelets and noticed a diamond and gold rolling ring bracelet, I quickly stopped and backed up almost stepping on a sales associates feet. "Oh, I'm so sorry," I said, "I didn't realize you were there, could we please see the tri-rolling ring bracelet, and do you have a tri-rolling ring to match?" Jackie and Michael turned around to look as she pulled it out of the case and set it on a red suede mat. "Today the bracelet is being offered at $48,700 U.S. dollars, and the matching ring is being offered at $13,100 U.S. dollars. Now the price does fluctuate slightly with the price of gold in the market."

"Well, Jackie, put them on let's see how they look," Michael said as I chimed in telling her I thought she should definitely get them as a memory of the trip while each ring could represent the three of our friendships. "Great, I'll take them both," Jackie said without hesitation as the girl stood there in disbelief watching her pull her American Express Platinum Card and passport from her fanny pack. Then out of nowhere chilled miniature glass bottles of Pierre water showed up, Champagne was offered along with various colors of French macaroons. I was waiting for red confetti to drop from the ceiling in celebration, but it didn't. We had just been inducted into the Cartier brotherhood of "If you have the money, we will take it" club.

"It's amazing what a little bit of sugar can do, isn't it?" I said as we walked out of the store laughing while Jackie wore her jewelry smiling and singing to the words of the famous song by Anita Ward, "You can ring my bell." I knew that was an anthem to her ex-husband.

I couldn't think of anything better right then than to go back to the Fouquet, take off my shoes, flop on the bed, and relax. We already had such a full day I could have just stayed in, ordered room service, and gone to bed early. But I couldn't; we were in Paris and with only a few days left in our trip, and I knew I needed to exercise control over my sleep deprivation and not lay down for too long.

As we all lay around in the room talking and laughing, Michael noticed the message light on the phone was lit up. So he pushed the button for the speaker phone and put in the message access code. It was the front desk calling. They had been able to secure tickets for us to the 9 p.m. showing at Moulin Rouge, which was the only availability for the whole week. We knew we didn't have any other choice but to go that night, or otherwise we would miss out.

"Okay," I said, "let's all get up go outside and walk around for a little bit, look at local shops in the area, maybe even go have a coffee to rev us up." Michael and Jackie agreed, so back outside we went to do some local exploring of the area.

"Look at this beautiful place," Jackie said pointing to a baroque store front painted a beautiful shade of celadon green. Looking up toward the awning at the entrance I saw the name Laduree written in gold. "This is it," I excitedly said. "This is the place where the original double-decker French macaroon was created!"

"Well what are we waiting for," Michael said. "Let's go

in!" While talking with the hostess we were able to find out the story behind the 1930 invention created by the grandson of Laduree, Pierre Desfontaines. The restaurant and tea house is regal and warm, set off by a

huge display of exquisitely displayed bakery items at its retail counter with the macaroon taking center stage. The multiple colors of the macaroons take your breath away, making it impossible to leave without at least having one. So we decided to take a table, have a cup of coffee and a macaroon chaser. Of course I had the coconut, Jackie had the rose petal, and Michael had the pistachio. I should have known one would not be enough. "Oh Fouquet," Michael said, "let's get a box!"

That sounds great, I said. "Let's have a pastry party tonight!"

"Sounds good to me" Jackie said with a smile, "I'm in!" Leaving the restaurant with a celadon-colored box filled with eighteen beautiful colors of macaroons made us feel like we had just purchased another box of jewels.

"Are you guys ready?" Jackie said as she walked out of her room with her hair teased higher than a male peacock's feathers during a mating dance. "Almost," I said looking up from putting on my shoes to see her standing there in a black leather skirt and a studded bustier top; she was obviously more than ready and excited for her night out at Moulin Rouge. Now I had been to Moulin Rouge many years earlier in my teens, which I still remember almost as a rite of passage. As a young man seeing partially naked women on stage in glitter thongs, propellered pasties and show lights makes you feel a little self-conscious as you do self-talk so you don't end up embarrassed looking like the spoon in the hot chocolate at Angelina's, straight up and stiff.

"I'm ready," Michael said appearing in the living room of our suite perfectly put together like he just walked out of a magazine. We were now locked and loaded, and the hotel town car was waiting downstairs to privately chauffer us around for the evening.

MOULIN ROUGE PARIS

When we arrived at Moulin Rouge, the outside foyer was full of people spilling out over the sidewalk and down the street in both directions. We asked our driver if he could pull up as close as possible to the entrance to let us out as we didn't want Jackie to have to walk unnecessarily far in her stacked up stilettos. He told us it would be no problem at all to get us up to the front as he slowly pushed people out of the way with the car. I then asked Michael what we were going to do since we were supposed to have tickets waiting for us. We didn't know if the large crowd of people also had tickets, were there to pick up their tickets, or were in a line to buy tickets. "Don't worry," he said, "we will figure it all out once we get out of the car."

It only took a couple of minutes more, and our driver stopped the car right in front of the theatre next to the velvet rope. He got out of the car, came around to the curb side, and opened the door. Michael got out first, then Jackie, and then me. The driver handed us his card with his cellular number and said to call him ten minutes before we were ready to be picked up and then drove off into the evening. The three of us were now standing there trying to figure out what to do, but that lasted all of about thirty seconds. "Good evening, Jackie, my name is Max," the bald mysterious man from the Fouquet Hotel said to Jackie. "Please, if the three of you would follow me this way, you will not be waiting in line, compliments of Emanuel." A security guard pulled back the velvet rope; the four of us walked through, and then he re hooked it.

"What is going on?" I asked Michael while walking through the double glass doors into the lobby. "This is crazy, do you remember he is the same guy that was loitering around the Fouquet when we checked in, and who is Emanuel?" I know God speaks in mysterious ways, but I was sure he didn't have a one-on-one with bald headed Max to give us VIP treatment at Moulin Rouge. Michael did remember the guy, but he also had no idea what was going on. Max showed us around the lobby for a few minutes while others were also standing in the lobby but being held back by velvet ropes. "I would like to now show you to your table so that you may order your drinks," Max said. He then walked us through another set of double doors that entered into the theater.

The stage was decorated and designed like an art deco dream out of the 1930s, sparkling in colored lights and creating energy in the room that let you know this was going to be a tantalizing and interesting event. "I have a VIP table reserved for you right over here," he said as he walked us up and around a few other pre seated tables filled with people drinking and laughing. Our table sat up a little higher than the others and was perfectly positioned to see and be seen. Max made sure we were all settled and then disappeared like before. The waiter arrived at our table taking our drink order within seconds of sitting down. We ordered our drinks as they sat the rest of the theatre and then the music began. "Ladies and gentlemen, welcome to Moulin Rouge," the announcer said filling the room with his voice while the lights went dim, the colored show lights came up, and out walked a parade of half-naked girls in pleather, pearls, boas and beads—the burlesque show had now begun.

Okay, so the show may have been a little sexually overt, as a man I would vote for seductive. If you're a woman, I don't know, I guess you would just have to be able to appreciate art in any form. Although they did throw in a few built-bodied males in skimpy thongs to try and balance out the load, which seemed only at those times did Jackie's interest level peak. But even with that I still don't think she liked it that every man's eyes in the room weren't looking at her.

When intermission broke, I told Jackie and Michael I needed to quickly go to the men's room, so I got up and made my way out through the lobby before the huge crowd broke. Once finished I walked back through the lobby to find Jackie by herself over at the other side of the foyer, standing at a concession table. As I started walking toward her I saw a hot pink boa around her neck while she held up a black and pink Moulin Rouge panty and tasseled pasties set. "Oh my god," I said to myself, "what is she doing?" I didn't want her to see me seeing her. Since Michael wasn't with her, I thought she might be trying to do this in private without us knowing. I took a quick left turn toward the opened auditorium doors and went back to find Michael sitting at the table.

"What's wrong?" Michael asked me.

"I don't know, I'm sort of in shock," I said. I then asked him if he knew where Jackie was, and he said no. "Well I do," I said with a nervous laugh. "I was walking back from the men's room and saw her standing alone in the crowd at the concession table looking like she was getting ready to buy a panty and pasties set. I told you both earlier today that we should have a pastry party tonight, not a pasties party!

"Oh crap!" Michael said. "Now look what you got us into!"

"Me? I didn't do anything, I just wanted to go back and eat some cookies later."

"Ya, well you're gonna get cookies all right. Got milk?" he said with his eyebrows arched up like the McDonald's logo, trying not to laugh. Of course I started nervously laughing so hard I couldn't stop while she was walking toward the table with her little bag of goodies. "What's so funny," she said looking at Michael.

"Oh nothing, Randy is just laughing about something he saw, I'm sure he'll tell you later." Luckily the lights dimmed again, and the second half of the show began, and I didn't have to say a word. Jackie ended up having more than enough glasses of wine to relax and distract her from remembering any plans she may have had for an evening back at the hotel room. Although I did give her a cookie with nuts before she went to sleep, I thought she would appreciate the gesture.

Our next few days in Paris were filled with more shopping, walking, and food while we held true to our word that we would help Jackie pick out some new

clothes for her new life. The first pieces for a new closet full of couture, at least we were hoping. Starting out at design houses such as Chanel, Christian Dior, Givenchy, and Jean Paul Gaultier, we were finding it harder than expected to locate haute couture, but prêt-à-porter was available. I reminded her that Paris fashion is at least a year or two ahead of anything else she would see back home, so prêt-à-porter it would be. French laces and mesh, Italian leathers and functional fabrics were the foundation for the collections she purchased. The dresses, blouses and pant suits were designed with pure lines and colors; she was now a fashion force to be reckoned with.

"So, Jackie, since today is Sunday and our last day in Paris, I would like to take you and Randy to church and then later tonight to one of my favorite restaurants, Le Soufflé."

ALEXANDER NEVSKY CATHEDRAL PARIS

"What do you think?" Michael said with excitement. I was happy to have a Sunday in Paris, and since it would be my first time going to church in another country, I was excited for the experience. So we all got ready and headed out the door of the hotel to have our Sunday in Paris. Hearing church bells ring invisibly throughout the city in glorious song was like seeing summer leaves on a tree dance in the warmth of a breeze. You don't know for sure where it's coming from, but you can feel it touch your body, deep within your being.

As it would be we ended up going to two different churches that day. The first was a morning service at Собор Александра Невского (A Russian Orthodox Cathedral

Alexander Nevsky) on 12 Rue Daru in Paris. It was established and consecrated in 1861 making it the first Russian Orthodox place of worship in France. The second church would be Notre Dame, a Catholic Church. When you walk into Alexander Nevsky Cathedral, you feel an extraordinary strong sense of sacred presence. Within a few minutes of sitting down for the service, Jackie decided to cross her legs, which caused an elderly French woman to get so upset she walked over to our row, pointed at her legs while shaking her finger, and told Jackie in French to sit up straight and uncross her legs.

Now although this wasn't a Catholic school, it still made me feel like I had just witnessed the disciplinary action of a nun. I was a little nervous after that, making sure I sat up straight and kept my legs together. It ended up to be a beautiful service giving me a cleansing feeling from the seductive world of entertainment I had experienced the night before at Moulin Rouge.

Once the church service was over we had the perfect Parisian sidewalk café lunch just across the Seine from Notre Dame on the left bank. As we sat there watching the fashionably dressed people of the Latin Quarter while lunching on our cheese board, bread, and French onion soup, the bells of Notre Dame started to ring. "Let's walk over to the Cathedral and see what's going on," Michael said. So we finished lunch and walked over. Just as we got there and walked in, the organ started to play, and the choir started to sing with angelic voices filling the air beyond the walls of the cathedral. It was so beautiful we sat down to listen for what seemed like ten minutes but was really an hour. I knew I had just had an appointment with God.

NOTRE DAME PARIS

We then spent the rest of the day meandering through shops, buying last-minutes travel gifts for people back home, while Michael got lucky in a once in a lifetime sale at the local Polo store. An unbelievably supple chestnut colored leather travel bag, something he really didn't know how badly he needed. Realizing now it was getting later than expected, we decided it would be a good idea to go back to the room and start organizing and packing. Especially since we knew Jackie's small warehouse of purchases was going to require some serious strategic thinking.

Now I've been told many times that I have the nose that knows, but this time I was not able to figure out what stunk so bad when we got back into our room. It smelled like rotten enchiladas with a hint of vinegar, but where was it coming from? I thought as I stood by the luggage in our room.

"Michael, do you smell that?" I asked when he walked out from helping Jackie in her room.

"Yes, it's really bad, have you brushed your teeth?" he said thinking he was really funny.

"No, I'm serious, Michael, something is dead over in this corner, and I think it's coming from your duffel bag." Michael walked over, and the closer he got I could tell by the look on his face he knew I was probably right. Picking up the bag, he unzipped it releasing out a plume of stench. "Oh my god!" I said. "That is old humid cat pee, that cat must have peed on your bag outside at that flee bitten hotel! And sure enough, it had peed all over the fabric zipper, causing it to seep into the fabric lining. I told Michael we were going to have to wash the bag and cut out the lining, otherwise he was going to have to throw the bag out. "I'm not throwing it out," he said looking at me like "don't even think about it."

"I almost got everything packed," Jackie announced walking into the room. "The only problem is I can't fit all of my shoes in my luggage." Michael told her not to worry he had a leather bag she could have for her shoes; he just needed to get it cleaned out. Thank goodness Michael had just bought the new bag at Ralph Lauren Paris, so it worked out perfect. I helped him wash up the cat pee sprayed bag with overly scented Parisian shower soap, then we cut out the lining, and Jackie never knew the difference.

We never told her what happened to the bag since we didn't want to make her feel like her ex-husband, having something that had been peed on. Plus it was all we could do since she didn't have any solutions, and it was now getting too late to shop. We had to start getting ready for dinner.

Michael was rushing us both because at this restaurant you can't show up even a minute late. Racing quickly to hurry up, we got down to the lobby only to find Jackie had forgotten her phone. "Oh no, I don't have my cell phone and I really need it. Do I have time to run back up to the room and quickly get it?" Jackie said looking at me.

"No you stay here with Michael and get the car, I will run up and get it. Where is it?" I said. She told me to look on her bathroom sink; she thought she left it in there. I took off walking fast back to the room as a text came through from Marie while I was in the elevator going up.

Marie was checking to see if we were successful in getting the medallion for Peter and to tell me that she just got a call from Arnoldo. Apparently the pool permitting at the villa had just been approved but would not be granted until the fountain I had purchased was removed. "What?" I texted back. "What are you talking about?" Marie texted back saying the man from the city hall came out to the villa and said before he would approve the permit, we had to agree and comply with two different concerns that he had. The first was the color of the pool. We could not have a swimming pool that was blue; it had to be green. Their reasoning was they do not want any more pools being built in the countryside that are blue because they can be seen by people in planes flying overhead, apparently ruining the natural visual beauty of the Tuscan landscape. Therefore, all pools have to now be green so they blend into the scenery.

Second, the fountain had to be removed because he claimed it didn't fit with the antiquity of the villa. I couldn't believe what I was reading, but we had no choice. We needed the pool. I texted back not to worry. We could use the fountain as a planter, or put it back in after the pool was finished and signed off. The most important thing now was just to play their game and get the pool in and finished before the fall weather arrived.

Finding myself distracted standing in the room, I needed to now locate Jackie's phone. I walked into her bathroom only to find the counter filled with everything else—brushes, perfume, makeup and more—but no phone. Knowing she would be upset if she didn't have it, I called Michael's phone to tell them I couldn't find it and asked him to please call her phone in hopes that it would ring. Then I stood there and waited. A few seconds went by, and then I heard a very faint and quiet vibrating noise coming from a purse. I opened the purse, and there it was. I grabbed the phone and ran out the door.

While quickly walking down the hall to get to the elevator, her phone started to send screen alerts; text messages were rolling in. I looked at her phone thinking Michael must be sending me a text from downstairs to see if I found her phone, but they weren't. The texts were from two different guys. The first was from Samuele and the second and third were from "E," and here is what they said.

> Baaabee where are you? How come you don't call me, did you get the roses? I miss you when are you coming home? Call me! Samuele

> Jackie, my princess, my Cinderella, my love...this is your prince, did the shoes fit? I'm anxiously waiting to hear. Amore —E

> Did you meet Max? How was Moulin Rouge? Waiting to feel the touch of your rose petal lips again. Tutto il mio amore —E

Oh great! I'm caught in her love triangle again. How does this happen? Why me, oh wait that text is signed by E. Who is it? What do I do now? I thought as the elevator descended, *I don't want her to know I saw these texts.* Quickly I turned her phone off, the doors opened, and there they both were waiting for me. "Get lucky," she said? I wanted to ask her the same question as I handed her the phone with a dark screen.

LE SOUFFLÉ PARIS

"Let's go," Michael said. "We don't want to be late".

We arrived at the quaint lacquered robin-egg blue storefront of Le Soufflé. The front door is flanked by half-draped windows and overhead scalloped awnings in celadon green trimmed in gold, which sets the stage for a true French culinary adventure. When you walk in you see very few tables, but all are covered in white table cloths with a beautiful yet understated elegant centerpiece of flowers to compliment the surrounding décor.

The word *soufflé* comes from the word *souffler*, which literally means "to blow." And it is more than apparent the chefs at Le Soufflé have mastered the art of puffing up egg whites to create entrees and desserts alike that are convincingly tiny miracles. They are light, they are savory, they are sweet, and they are beautiful. So beautiful in fact that I had to take pictures. I was now officially the tacky tourist who takes pictures of his food, but I had to because I have never seen soufflés so big and perfectly golden in my life. We each ordered a savory soufflé followed by a sweet soufflé.

"What are you doing?" Jackie asked me as she saw me fiddling around under the table with my hands. I didn't need her calling me out. I was partially unzipping then unbuttoning the top button of my pants and pulling out my shirt to cover it. Trying to be discreet without anyone knowing the difference so when I stood up to leave it would look like intentional fashion. I had eaten way too much. The egg whites fooled me. So I told them, to which they agreed they felt the same way.

Once we finished we decided to walk back to our hotel rather than call for the car. We were going to try and walk this off. But for me that didn't turn out to be such a good idea. We didn't get but maybe three blocks down the street, and I had to yell out to Michael and Jackie to hurry and flag down a cab. I had to get back to the hotel right now; my stomach was ready to become the literal definition of soufflé. It was getting ready to blow!

If the soufflés the night before were a small miracle, then getting to the airport and on to the plane the next morning was a supernatural phenomenon. I don't know how we did it, but we did. "Good morning, ladies and gentlemen, and welcome to Air France Flight 3622. We will be departing in just a few minutes, so if you will, please make sure your seat belts are fastened and your seatbacks and tray tables are in their full upright position. We will be coming through the cabin to collect all service items at this time. We hope you enjoy your flight with us today," the flight attendant said as we settled in for our return transatlantic flight.

About halfway through the flight Jackie turned over to me and said, "What would you think if I asked Emanuel to find me a pair of shoes to match my leather belt I bought?"

"Which leather belt?" I said?

"You know the one I bought from him at his store in Florence."

"But I thought his name was Manuel."

"Oh, it is," she said. "I just think sometimes the e is silent."

Oh really, I wanted to say, sort of like you've been about it?

CHAPTER 12

Tuscany...Next Left

We arrived back home the same day we left, but in the midafternoon. And although I was really tired I wanted to drop by Mark and Marie's house on my way home and give Marie the medallion I had picked up for Peter. It was a beautiful summer day, the sun was shining, and all the kids and their friends were out having a great time in the pool. "Peter, come up here," Marie said. "I have something for you that Uncle Randy brought back from Rome that was blessed by the pope." Peter jumped out of the pool and came over to the patio by the house. Marie gave him the medallion and told him it was a gift from her and his dad, in honor of his confirmation. She went on to tell him it was a medallion of the Archangel Michael, his confirmation name. I couldn't believe what I was hearing. My heart sank, and I felt sick. It was not Michael, and she had never told me he had a confirmation name, let alone the name Michael. She had just said he had been confirmed. How would I even know there was also a confirmation name involved? I didn't know what to say or if I should say anything. No one looked that closely at the details, which almost required magnification anyway, so I left not saying a word.

When I got home I could not get it out of my mind, and I kept playing that phone call Marie had placed to me in Rome over and over in my mind. I called Michael to confirm what had happened on that call in Rome, and he confirmed it with me that Marie never told us a confirmation name, and that yes we did buy the medallion of St. Peter. I was so restless all afternoon knowing what they thought they had, they actually didn't have, and I felt terrible. So I got in the car and drove back over to their house. I told Marie I needed to talk with her in private. She asked me what was wrong. She knew I was upset, but I told her just too please sit down I just needed to talk with her for a minutes, and then I told her the whole story.

When I was done telling her the story, she looked at me and said, "Oh no, Randy, the medallion is St. Michael."

"No, Marie, it's not," I said. "It's St. Peter, that's what I'm trying to tell you." Marie looked at me with a big smile and said, "I looked at it closely after you left, and it is St. Michael, he is holding a sword." I sat there in disbelief, knowing the soufflé had been trumped; this was actually the tiny miracle.

About five months later I got a call from my brother early one morning, "Hey, Randy, are you awake?"

"I am now," I said.

"What's up?"

"Well," he went on to say, "you're not going to believe it, Samuele's divorce is final."

"We'll thank you for waking me up to give me the announcement."

"No, just listen," he said. Part of his divorce agreement with Tina was that she got three final weeks at the villa, but she had to use them before the end of the year.

"So what's the problem?" I asked.

"I'm going to tell you, just hold on."

"I'm holding," I said. And here is what he said.

"Close to four months ago Tina decided to make a deal with an auctioneer friend of hers to auction off the villa at a fundraiser, it was something for injured animals, and I think it was called Dogs with Dignity. Anyway it was a big scam, she had no intention of ever using the villa; she just wanted to make money off of it for herself. So the deal she made was she got to keep fifty percent of whatever money they could raise for a one-week stay at the villa. They ended up making five thousand dollars on it, so she got to keep twenty five hundred for herself." I told Mark I couldn't believe what I was hearing. Then he told me it even got worse.

"Three weeks ago, while Samuele was in Italy he decided to stay at the villa with a girlfriend of his. He was trying to figure out if he was going to continue the relationship or break it off. He thought since he was going to be in Florence anyway, he would just stay at the villa with her and at the same time could make sure everything went ok for the people who were also staying there that week, the winners of the auction. Oh and their name is Stacy and George Vineland, if you can even believe it."

"So the Vineland's are staying at the vineyard," I said. "Okay, I just want to keep this straight, go ahead."

"To make things even more complicated, Peter had gone over to visit his friend Angela from New York. She was in Venice working in an art gallery doing an internship for college since she is very interested in art and art history. So he arranged to take her to Rome to see private artwork at the Vatican and then planned to host her at the villa for a few days, something he had always wanted to do but never had the chance to do until now while having no idea anyone was staying at the villa.

"In the meantime Samuele and his girlfriend, Sienna, took the master bedroom and had all of their stuff set up in there. Samuele then decided to take Sienna to the beach for an overnight stay, never thinking it would have probably been a better idea to wait until the Vinelands showed up and help them get settled, but he didn't. Within hours of Samuele and Sienna leaving, Stacy and George show up with three other couples they decided to invite, even though the rules for the auction prize were only for one couple for seven days. They wanted to act like big shots and invite all these other people and told them they would treat them to a week at a villa in Tuscany, and all it would cost them would be the flight.

"Of course Stacy and George also decided they were going to sleep in the master bedroom, even though there are eight other queen size beds in the house, while obviously forgetting or not caring that this is someone's private home. So Stacy walks into the master bedroom and sees all of Sienna and Samuele's clothes and stuff all over and is furious, she can't believe someone's stuff has been left in the room. So like the complete idiot that she is, she picks up everything and throws it into a pile out in the terrace bedroom, then proceeds to set up all of her and George's stuff in the room. Their friends take another bedroom down the hall and two of the bedrooms in the apartment side of the villa. Once they are settled in they have their first night of partying with their friends. They drink seven bottles of wine out of our private wine collection, they break a bottle of olive oil all over the kitchen then wipe it up with Marie's best white linen napkins, and they break the handle off of the drawer of the kitchen hutch."

"The next morning the Vinelands and their friends decide to take a day trip into Florence, and Samuele decides he wants to take Sienna to the French Riviera for two days, which is only about five hours away. But before they go he wanted to go back to the villa to get more clothes and check in with the Vinelands to make sure everything was going okay. When he got back to the villa they were gone, and he found all of his and Sienna's stuff in a big heaping pile on the floor in the terrace bedroom, a room that has three beds, and he was mad. So he picks up all of their stuff and brings it back into the master bedroom and throws all of Stacy and Georges stuff into big pig piles out into the terrace room, and then they leave to the Rivera.

"Now during all of this, Peter is in Venice with Angela and just happens to be on Facebook and see's that Samuele has told his daughter Sophia, who is also Peter's friend that he is going to be in town with Sienna. Samuele tells her some people won an auction for a week at the villa, so he will be staying there to make sure everything goes okay. Peter was really upset because he was now getting ready to leave from Venice with Angela to the villa. So Peter called me and asked me what was going on."

"Did you even know?" I asked Mark.

"I had just found out the night before when Samuele called me to tell me he had made it to the villa and about the people and his clothes, he said he just then remembered he had forgotten to tell me about the auction."

"Really," I said. "Okay, then what happened?"

"Well I just told Peter there was nothing I could do from here, so he needed to call Samuele and work it out. So Peter called Samuele, who was now in Monte Carlo to find out what was going on.

"Samuele say's to Peter, "Baaabee don't worry, this is your house, you come bring Angela, and everything will be worked out. You and Angela can have the whole apartment, I will see you there."

"So Peter and Angela jump on the train and come to the villa. In the meantime Samuele called Maria the housekeeper even though it was her day off and asked her to take all of George and Stay's friends stuff out of the apartment and put it into the terrace room and to get the apartment clean and ready for Peter and Angela. He also told her not to worry about cleaning up the villa, she could do that tomorrow.

"Peter and Angela now show up, they don't know anything about what has transpired, but Peter notices when he walks in that the main part of the villa is a mess. Nice linens are wadded up and thrown in the corner on the floor, the trash is overflowing with wine bottles, and dirty dishes are stacked in the sink. He was so embarrassed and mad he just turned around and told Angela that Samuele would take care of it. Then they put all his and Angela's stuff into the apartment and left to go into town for a while. Then the Vinelands and their friends show up to find all of their stuff is combined and thrown into the terrace room. Furious they go into the apartment and start going through all of Peter and Angela's luggage and find Peter's passport and take it. Once Stacy sees the name on the passport she goes into the laundry room and see's my name on the emergency contact list and calls me. I told her there was nothing I could do, I wasn't even involved, and it would probably be best if they all just left and found a hotel. I reminded her it was our private home, and by the sounds of it they were treating our home like one from a rental pool. She started yelling at me so I told her they just needed to leave. Right then Peter and Angela walked in to the villa to find the Vineland's and their friends standing in the great room. George and Stacy started yelling at Peter, telling him he was a spoiled brat, and he had no right to throw all of their stuff in a pile out in the terrace room. Peter was in shock, he didn't even know what hit him, and he had nothing to do with any of it. They kept yelling at him telling him he was a spoiled kid born with a golden spoon in his mouth. Peter was so mad he kicked them all out of the villa right then. I guess he also yelled at them that they were nothing but a bunch of low-class pigs when they were trying to get all their stuff out the door and into their car."

I was laughing in disbelief while Mark was telling me all of this. Then I asked him if they said anything else. Mark said Stacy yelled back to Peter, "We are not low class."

Well," I told Mark, "I guess she just confirmed they're pigs!"

That night I fell asleep thinking about everything that happened and started dreaming about driving through the countryside of Italy while listening to music in my vintage Fiat. Up ahead on the side of the road I came upon a rental Fiat full of people and luggage, something very familiar to me. I stopped to ask them if they needed help. The man driving the car said they had just got to town for what was to be their trip of a lifetime as he sat there with a map in his hand. I asked him where they were going. "Well he said, we just pulled over to look at this map, we're on our way to Tuscany. Do you know where it is?" I told him I absolutely did, and if he kept driving through the country in this direction about another five miles, he will come upon an old wooden sign that says, "Tuscany...Next Left."

Early the next morning I was awoken out of the dream by my cell phone, and by the time I found it I had missed the call. Looking at the screen to see if there was a message registered, it showed I had two missed calls and one message. Pressing the play button wondering who it could be, I heard Jackie's voice cutting in and out on the voice-recorded message. "Randy, it's Ja-ckie; I'm on my way to the a-port. I got a call this m-or-ing from...e-eh-e. He asked me to meet him in Fl-ence so I'm get-ing on a pla-n now, ca me!"

I sat there in my chair wondering whom it was she was going to see knowing in my heart it had to be one of two men. Should I try and call her back right now? I thought. Or did it really matter? I knew I had clearly heard through the silent letters of her words she had made a left turn toward her heart.

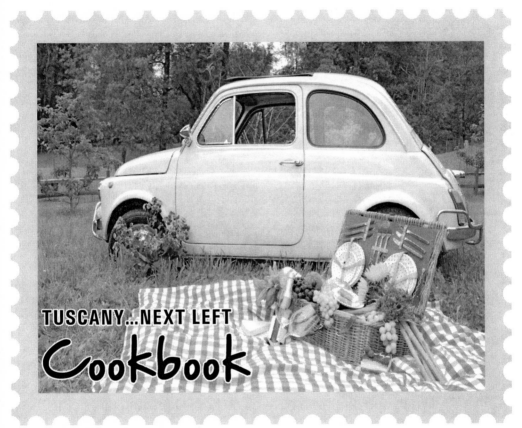

TUSCANY...NEXT LEFT
Cookbook

Appetizer
Campania Eggplant Stack

Makes 6 towers

Ingredients:

Aubergine eggplant cut into 12 single 1/3 inch slices

3 large ripe tomatoes

12 fresh basil leaves

6 thin slices of mozzarella

Spice Mixture: 3 pinches salt, 6 turns pepper, 3 teaspoons finely chopped oregano, 3 teaspoons finely chopped thyme

Extra Virgin Olive Oil

Aged Balsamic Vinegar

Toothpicks

Preparation:

Brush eggplant with olive oil on both sides and grill both sides for several minutes until tender. Cover a cookie sheet with non-stick baking paper, loosely arranging 6 eggplant slices. Pre heat oven to 200 F then gently dust eggplant with half of herb mixture. Next slice each tomato into 4 even slices, placing one slice on top of each eggplant. Add one basil leaf to each tomato slice and sprinkle again with half of remaining spice mixture. Add remaining eggplant, then tomato to each stack again sprinkle with remaining spice mixture. Top each tower with one slice of mozzarella cheese and basil leaf.

Place toothpick in the center through the tower then gently drizzle aged balsamic and olive oil over tower. Place in oven until tomatoes are warm and mozzarella is melted.

Appetizer
Roman Stuffed Olives

Makes 24

Ingredients:

2 ounces prosciutto

1 ounce mild blue cheese

24 pitted Spanish olives

4 cups frying oil

½ cup all-purpose flour

1 large egg beaten to blend

1 cup dry white wine

Olive Oil

3 tablespoons fresh grated parmigiana Reggiano

½ cup fine dry bread crumbs

Preparation:

Slice prosciutto into very small pieces then sauté in olive oil adding a little salt and pepper cooking until golden. Then lower the heat and add white wine, let simmer for about 30 minutes adding a small amount of water if necessary to keep from drying out. Remove and drain from pan onto paper towels, gently patting dry.

Place room temperature blue cheese into a small bowl blending in sautéed prosciutto and 1 ½ tablespoons parmigiana. Fill each pitted olive with mixture and set aside. Next pour cooking oil into a deep skillet so that oil will cover olives, heat oil to 350. Next roll stuffed olives into flour then in blended egg and then into bread crumbs completely covering.

Fry olives for about 30 seconds or until golden brown. Remove with a strainer spoon and place on paper towel to drain, then arrange on your favorite serving dish sprinkling remaining parmigiana over olives and serve warm.

Appetizer
Amalfi Mascarpone Dip

Ingredients:

8 ounces mascarpone cheese

12 large green olives finely diced

1 7oz. can Asdo Mar Tuna in olive oil drained

5 finely chopped anchovy fillets

4 finely chopped scallions

Pepper

Crostini

Preparation:

Add all ingredients in order as shown into bowl and mix with a fork until all is blended, Add a few turns of pepper to top. Serve with crostini and with your favorite Crudités.

Drink
Sorrento Limencello

Ingredients:

15 Lemons (medium size)

6 ½ cups Everclear 151 proof or 190 proof where available

6 ½ cups water

5 ¼ cups granulated sugar

Supplies:

2 large glass containers with lids

1 wooden spoon

Cheese cloth

1 potato peeler

1 funnel

1 ladle

Glass bottles for bottling

Time to make: 2 months

Preparation:

Wash lemons and peel, be very careful to only get the yellow peel and not the white pith under the skin. Place peels into large glass jar and add 6 ½ cups of Everclear grain alcohol. Gently stir peels making sure all are submerged and covered in the alcohol. Put lid on jar and place in a cool area without sunlight. Let rest for 2 weeks, then gently stir once and replace lid, let rest for 2 more weeks.

At 4 weeks put 6 ½ cups water in sauce pan and heat but do not boil adding in 5 ½ cups granulated sugar and stir until completely dissolved, let cool. Pour cooled solution into your jar of lemon peels and alcohol. Gently stir twice, again making sure all peels are covered. Put lid back on jar and let rest for 2 weeks, then gently stir once and replace lid, let rest for 2 more weeks.

Put water moistened cheese cloth over the opening of your second glass jar and slowly pour your mixture through the cloth into the jar straining out all sediment. Now you are ready to bottle. Use your ladle and funnel for bottling which will help to avoid overflow and spilling. Once your Limencello is bottled place bottles into the freezer for storage.

Dessert
Limencello Tiramisù di Capri

Ingredients:

16oz mascarpone cheese, softened

1 cup heavy cream

6 lemons (use for juice and zest)

2 tablespoons fresh lemon zest

1 cup lemon curd

½ cup confectioners' sugar

1 ½ cups Limencello

¾ cup fresh lemon juice

1 cup water

1/3 cup sugar

40 ladyfingers (Savoiardi)

13x9inch glass dish

Preparation:

In a large bowl mix 16oz mascarpone cheese, 1 tablespoon fresh lemon zest, 1 cup lemon curd, ½ cup confectioners' sugar, 1cup heavy cream, ½ cup Limencello. Blend until smooth with soft peaks then set aside.

In a saucepan heat remaining Limencello, ¾ cup fresh lemon juice, 1 cup water then gently pour in 1/3 cup sugar stirring until dissolved then slightly cool down mixture and pour into small pan no deeper than ¼ inch.

Take each ladyfinger and roll into sauce, quickly remove so it doesn't fall apart, then place tightly side by side filling the bottom of a 13x9inch glass dish. Spoon half of the lemon cream mixture over the top of the lady fingers completely covering all corners. Repeat process with lady fingers and lemon cream one more time then gently sprinkle remaining lemon zest over the top. Cover glass dish with plastic wrap and cool for no less than six hours.

Entrée
Gubbio Pasta Salumi

Ingredients:

1/4 lb each Genoa and hard salami

2cups penne pasta

1egg

Pepperoncino flakes

2 cups smokes Gouda with jalapeños

1cup Gorgonzola

2 chopped cloves garlic

Preparation:

In large skillet put in olive oil and heat adding chopped garlic sautéing until brown then add chopped salami a pinch pepperoncino flakes 4 turns of black pepper sauté until lightly crispy on medium high heat at the same time start pasta water 6 cups bring to boil add pasta add a little pasta water to skillet with salami to reduce carmelization in bottom of skillet.

Cook pasta until al dente put skillet aside when pasta is ready put skillet back onto medium heat strain pasta and put directly into skillet stir pasta into salami and putting a couple more tablespoons pasta water into skillet; add the egg and stir until egg is cooked…turn heat off add Gorgonzola stir next add Gouda stir until melted coating all you pasta and Salumi pieces serve…makes four servings sprinkle with fresh chopped Italian parsley.

Dessert
La Dolce Vita Panna Cotta

Ingredients:

1 tablespoon unflavored gelatin

1 cup half and half

3 cups heavy whipping cream

1/3 cup sugar

1 tablespoon honey

1 ½ teaspoons vanilla extract

Directions:

In a saucepan add half and half and sprinkle gelatin over the half and half and let sit for 5 minutes. Now place saucepan on burner on medium heat and stir, do not let it come to a boil, making sure all gelatin is dissolved, this should take about another 5 minutes. Add the cream, sugar, honey and vanilla extract. Stir for another 5 minutes until sugar is dissolved.

Take eight ramekins and spray with vegetable oil, then filling with ½ cup if mixture. Place in refrigerator for at least 4 hours.

Sauce:

2 1/2 cups fresh raspberries

4 tablespoons granulated sugar

1/3 cup water

2 teaspoons fresh lemon juice

Directions:

In small saucepan add water and bring up to warm, do not boil. Add sugar and stir until dissolved, add lemon juice stir and remove from heat. Put raspberries into food processor and add syrup, process until smooth then strain through a fine mesh sieve. Cool to room temperature.

Take a small knife around the edge of the ramekins to loosen panna cotta, turn upside down onto plate, drizzle with raspberry sauce and remaining fresh raspberries.

Dessert
Parisian Peach Melba

Ingredients:

4 firm ripe peaches

2 cups water

1 ½ cups granulated sugar

¼ vanilla bean (seeds removed to add separately)

1/2 cup peach liquor

Vanilla Bean Ice Cream

Mint sprigs

Chocolate hazelnut pirouettes

24 raspberries

Preparation:

Put an (X) at the bottom of each peach with a knife. In a small saucepan combine water, sugar, peach liquor, vanilla pod, vanilla seeds, bring to boil on medium heat, add peaches. Boil peaches in syrup for 2 minutes and reduce heat to simmer for 5 minutes. Remove peaches from syrup with slotted spoon and cool on cutting board. Peel peaches starting with the (X) end, cut in half, remove pit. Put halves into glass bowl.

Bring syrup mixture back up to boil for 10 minutes, drizzle syrup over peaches until lightly covered and discard unused syrup. Refrigerate peaches covered until cold.

Raspberry Coulis:

    1 ½ cups fresh raspberries

    ½ cup sugar

    2 teaspoons fresh lemon juice

    1/3 cup water

Directions:

In small saucepan add water and bring up to warm, do not boil. Add sugar and stir until dissolved, add lemon juice stir and remove from heat. Put raspberries into food processor and add syrup, process until smooth then strain through a fine mesh sieve. Cool to room temperature.

Serve:

I like to use a margarita glass but you can also use a bowl. Place one scoop of vanilla ice cream into glass, lay ½ peach pitted side down onto corner of ice cream. Drizzle peach and ice cream with raspberry coulis, place mint sprig and three raspberries onto ice cream along with one pirouette and serve.

ABOUT THE AUTHOR

Randall Steven Altig is a true renaissance man in every sense of the word. As an Emmy nominated network television host of his own show, Maximum Living, he has been able to inspire countless numbers of people with humorous stories from his unique outlook on life. As a self-described Lifestyle Architect, he has mastered the art of living, from "The property line to the waistline", giving viewers and readers alike an opportunity to escape their everyday world while learning new ideas of how to change theirs for the better.

Randall Steven knows the importance of maximizing opportunities and experiences in life while at the same time he is highly aware of the challenges that face each of us every day. He says, "If you can step back from your life and look in on it as a director of your own movie, you will be empowered to make changes in your steps that can transform the world in and around you."